Csaba Balogh

Greatest 550 puzzles

From practical games of 2017

Chess
Evolution

Responsible editor
Csaba Balogh

Cover designer
Piotr Pielach

Typesetting
Piotr Pielach ‹www.i-press.pl›

First edition 2018 by Chess Evolution

Greatest 550 puzzles. From practical games of 2017
Copyright © 2018 Chess Evolution

ISBN: 978-615-5793-02-8

All sales or enquiries should be directed to Chess Evolution
2040 Budaors, Nyar utca 16, Hungary

e-mail: info@chess-evolution.com
website: www.chess-evolution.com

Printed in Hungary

TABLE OF CONTENTS

KEY TO SYMBOLS

=   Equality or equal chances

⩲   White has a slight advantage

⩱   Black has a slight advantage

±   White is better

∓   Black is better

+-   White has a decisive advantage

-+   Black has a decisive advantage

∞   unclear

⯬   with compensation

⇆   with counterplay

↑   with initiative

→   with an attack

△   with the idea

□   only move

N   novelty

!   a good move

!!   an excellent move

?   a weak move

??   a blunder

!?   an interesing move

?!   a dubious move

+   check

mate

PREFACE

As a professional chess player, I know exactly how important it is to perform well in tactical calculations. We face them so often that after playing a great game, we can simply blunder something and throw away a safe point, causing ourself sleepless nights!

For most of the players and chess fans, the biggest pleasure in a chessgame is to beat an opponent with a beautiful combination, of which we can be proud at. However to live with all the given oportunities and not miss any of the chances, we must stay in sharp shape all the time, what we can reach only by practicing puzzlesolving.

Many puzzle books are based on artificial positions or selected only for their beauty. The concept of my book is different. The highest priority is to **"use the practical side of the puzzles" and take the level of calculation to a completely new dimension.**

All the puzzles have been selected from recent games, trying to put the reader in the shoes of "the player".

The difficulty of the different sections might also give you a right evaluation of your current tactical skills and bring them further ahead.

I tried to mix three things in my book:
      1. a lot of fun in solving the puzzles,
      2. a lot of different tactical ideas,
      3. and of course, the direct practical use for your future games.

A very important factor to keep in mind — all the **practical motifs from the book can definitely be used in your future games!**

Enjoy!

Csaba Balogh

INTRODUCTION

USEFUL INFORMATION FOR OUR DEAR READERS

This book is the continuation of the successful puzzle-book series, which started with the "Greatest 365 Puzzles" and "Greatest 501 Puzzles" from the practical games of 2012. It was followed by „Tactics, Tactics, Tactics!" Volume 3 and Volume 4 which covered the best practical puzzles of 2013–2015 and the next one of the series was the „Greatest 551 Puzzles" with the combinations of 2016.

The new book contains 550 puzzles divided into 3 chapters. You will find a huge range of tactical ideas that you can use in your own games! All the puzzles have been collected from practical games throughout 2017. In each section the puzzles are sorted according to the date of the game.

The book consists of three chapters:
1. **Easy (300 Puzzles)**
2. **Medium (178 Puzzles)**
3. **Hard (72 Puzzles)**

All in all 550 puzzles created by the greatest masters of our time, such as Carlsen, Caruana, Aronian, Kramnik, Anand and many more.

I advise you to try to solve all the combinations in each chapter one-by-one, because a less difficult solution from the „Easy" section might be even more brilliant from the beauty point of view than a „nutcracker" from the „Hard" ones. Even if a puzzle can be easily solved, it sharpens your tactical skills and makes it so much easier to find solutions in a practical game, even under difficult circumstances.

To be tactically sharp is one of the basic requirements for a successful chess player!

[1]

▷ **U. Kersten**
► **S. Fedorchuk**
Staufer Open, 02.01.2017

1.+-

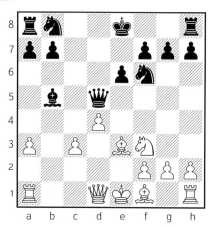

[2]

▷ **A. Heimann**
► **B. Stillger**
Basel Open, 04.01.2017

1.+-

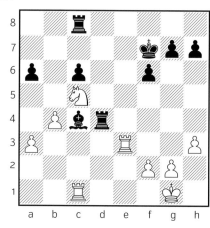

[3]

▷ **D. Svetushkin**
► **D. Forcen Esteban**
Roquetas de Mar Open, 05.01.2017

1.+-

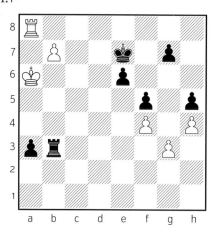

[4]

▷ **E. Safarli**
► **A. Donchenko**
Basel Open, 05.01.2017

1.+-

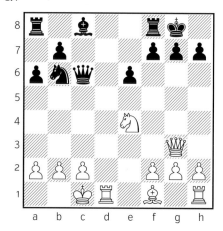

[5]

▷ R. Kevlishvili
► C. Bauer
Basel Open, 05.01.2017

1...−+

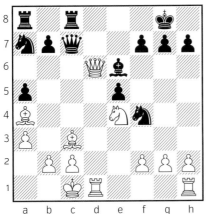

[6]

▷ M. Antipov
► S. Ivanov
Rilton Cup Stockholm, 05.01.2017

1.+−

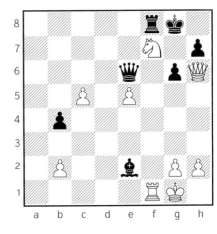

[7]

▷ J. Hammer
► R. Elseth
NCB Sandefjord, 06.01.2017

1. +/−

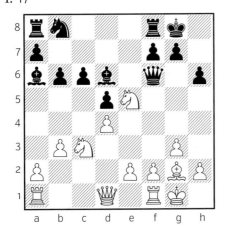

[8]

▷ K. Piorun
► W. Przybylski
Polish Championship Rapid, 08.01.2017

1.+−

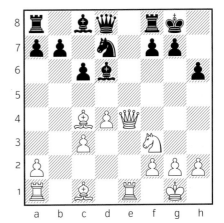

(9)

▷ **S. Gajewski**
► **B. Socko**
Polish Championship Rapid, 08.01.2017

1...–+

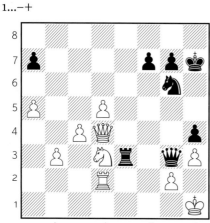

(10)

▷ **L. Dek**
► **G. Meier**
Internet PRO League Rapid, 11.01.2017

1...–+

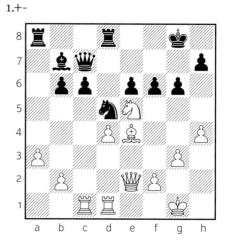

(11)

▷ **H. Gabuzyan**
► **S. Ter Sahakyan**
Armenian League Yerevan, 16.01.2017

1...–+

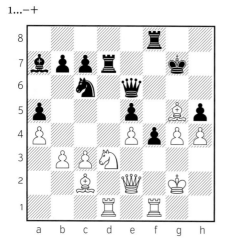

(12)

▷ **S. Mareco**
► **M. Leskovar**
Internet PRO League Rapid, 18.01.2017

1.+-

(13)

▷ **R. Jumabayev**
► **A. Yatzenko**
Internet PRO League Rapid, 18.01.2017

1...–+

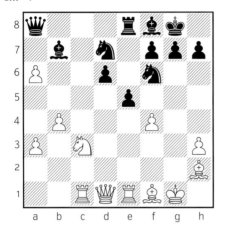

(14)

▷ **S. Lu**
► **J. Van Foreest**
Wijk aan Zee, 20.01.2017

1.+-

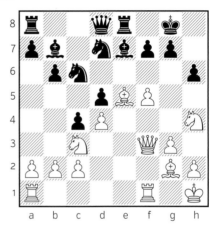

(15)

▷ **E. Hansen**
► **J. Xiong**
Wijk aan Zee, 20.01.2017

1.+-

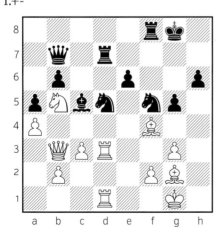

(16)

▷ **S. Sethuraman**
► **K. Sundararajan**
Gibraltar Masters, 25.01.2017

1. +/-

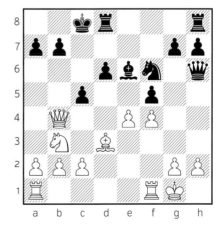

(17)

▷ **L. Dek**
► **E. Bacrot**
Internet Pro League Rapid, 25.01.2017

1...−+

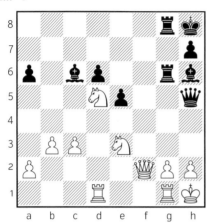

(18)

▷ **J. Salomon**
► **M. Vachier-Lagrave**
Gibraltar Masters, 26.01.2017

1...−+

(19)

▷ **B. Gledura**
► **H. Nakamura**
Gibraltar Masters, 27.01.2017

1...−+

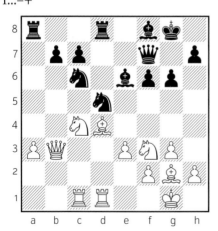

(20)

▷ **H. Nakamura**
► **E. Iturrizaga Bonelli**
Gibraltar Masters, 28.01.2017

1.+−

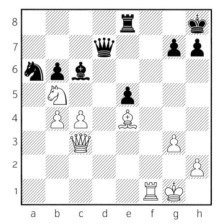

[21]

▷ S. Sethuraman
► I. Cheparinov
Gibraltar Masters, 29.01.2017

1...−+

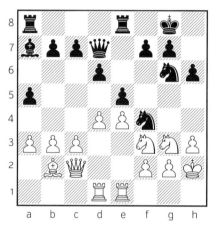

[22]

▷ S. Docx
► S. Sethuraman
Gibraltar Masters, 30.01.2017

1...−+

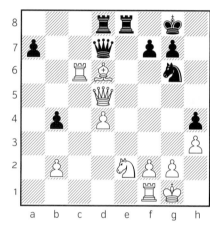

[23]

▷ Z. Izoria
► J. Sheng
Internet Pro League Rapid, 01.02.2017

1...−+

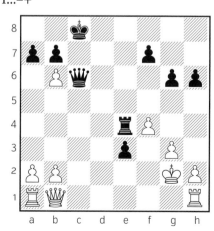

[24]

▷ I. Cheparinov
► D. Fridman
Gibraltar Masters, 01.02.2017

1.+−

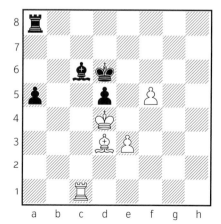

(25)

▷ **B. Gledura**
► **V. Topalov**
Gibraltar Masters, 02.02.2017

1...−+

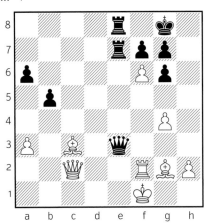

(26)

▷ **E. Espinosa Veloz**
► **C. Gomes Garrido**
Cuban Championship, 02.02.2017

1...−+

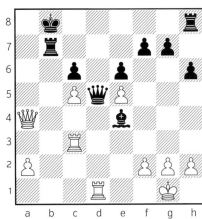

(27)

▷ **A. Donchenko**
► **A. Naiditsch**
Gibraltar Masters, 02.02.2017

1...−+

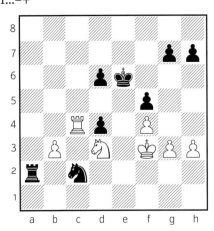

(28)

▷ **J. Martinez Lopez**
► **J. Mendez Guerra**
Catalan League, 04.02.2017

1.+−

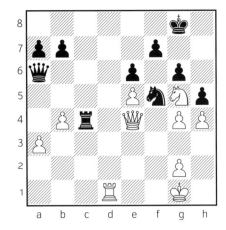

(29)

▷ **N. Grandelius**
► **S. Ivanov**
Swedish League, 04.02.2017

1.+-

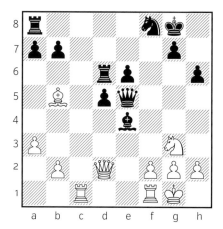

(30)

▷ **W. So**
► **M. Vachier-Lagrave**
Internet Pro League Rapid, 11.02.2017

1.+-

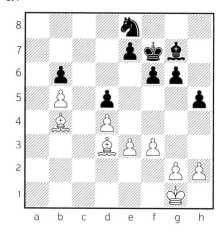

(31)

▷ **J. Quesada Perez**
► **L. Van Wely**
Internet PRO League Rapid, 11.02.2017

1.+-

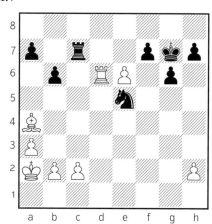

(32)

▷ **M. Ragger**
► **J. Maiwald**
Bundesliga, 18.02.2017

1.+-

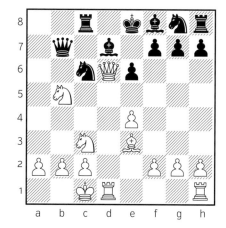

(33)

▷ S. Bromberger
► N. Grandelius
Bundesliga, 19.02.2017

1.+-

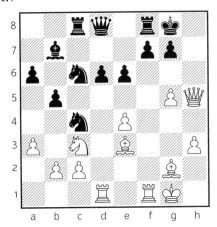

(34)

▷ S. Bogdanovish
► V. Onischuk
Nebesna Sotnya Rapid, 19.02.2017

1.+-

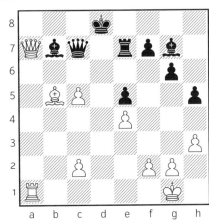

(35)

▷ M. Bezold
► L. Mc Shane
Bundesliga, 19.02.2017

1...-/+

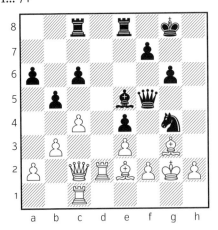

(36)

▷ A. Motylev
► A. Donchenko
Aeroflot Open Moscow, 21.02.2017

1.+-

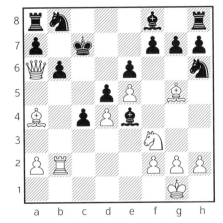

[37]

▷ **A. Riazantsev**
► **D. Jakovenko**
Sharjah FIDE GP, 22.02.2017

1...−+

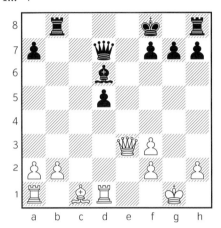

[38]

▷ **V. Durarbayli**
► **K. Dragun**
Internet Pro League Rapid, 22.02.2017

1...−+

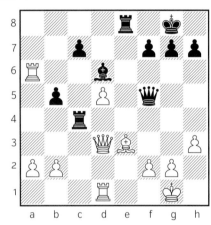

[39]

▷ **M. Cornette**
► **M. Nikolov**
Rochefort Open, 22.02.2017

1...−+

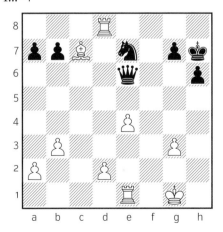

[40]

▷ **A. Kosteniuk**
► **A. Muzychuk**
Fide World Cup Teheran, 23.02.2017

1...−+

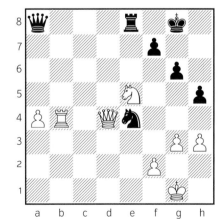

[41]

▷ D. Harika
► Z. Tan
Fide World Cup Teheran, 25.02.2017

1.+-

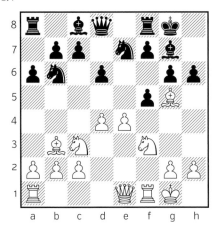

[42]

▷ R. Buhmann
► N. Vitiugov
Aeroflot Open Moscow, 25.02.2017

1...−+

[43]

▷ R. Cvek
► V. Laznicka
Czech League, 26.02.2017

1...−+

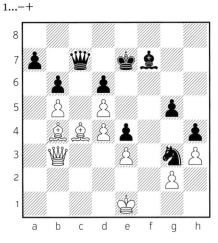

[44]

▷ M. Pavlovic
► S. Swapnil
Aeroflot Open Moscow, 27.02.2017

1...−+

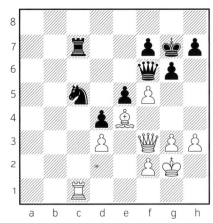

(45)

▷ P. Maghsoodloo
► D. Paravyan
Aeroflot Open Moscow, 01.03.2017

1...−+

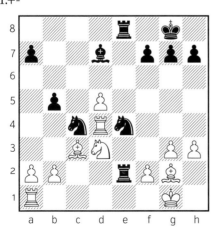

(46)

▷ K. Lie
► O. Saevareid
Norwegian League, 03.03.2017

1.+−

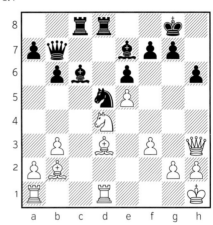

(47)

▷ I. Nikolaidis
► A. Karagiannis
Greek Championship, 04.03.2017

1.+−

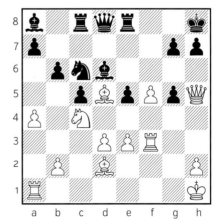

(48)

▷ T. Hillarp Persson
► D. Fendrich
Swedish League, 04.03.2017

1.+−

[49]

▷ S. Lorparizangeneh
► P. Darini
Iranian Championship, 05.03.2017

1...−+

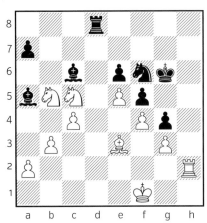

[50]

▷ R. Jumabayev
► A. Shabalov
Jurmala Tal Mem Rapid, 05.03.2017

1.+−

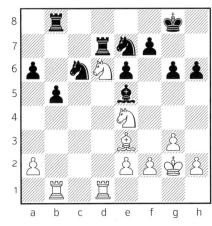

[51]

▷ S. Ganguly
► S. Lu
India-China Liaocheng, 07.03.2017

1...−+

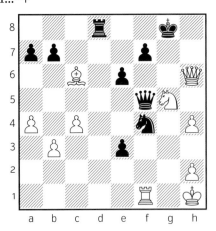

[52]

▷ M. Bagheri
► P. Maghsoodloo
Iranian Championship, 07.03.2017

1...−+

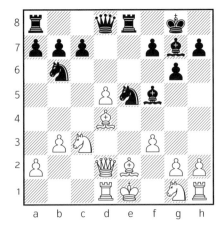

(53)

▷ **G. Jones**
► **C. Henriquez Villagra**
Internet Pro League Rapid, 08.03.2017

1.+-

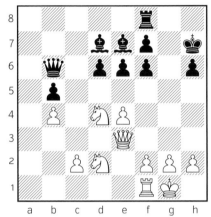

(54)

▷ **E. Agrest**
► **N. Pert**
Internet Rapid, 08.03.2017

1.+-

(55)

▷ **S. Lorparizangeneh**
► **S. Mousavi**
Iranian Championship, 12.03.2017

1...−+

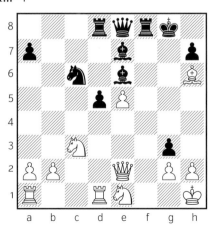

(56)

▷ **M. Gagunashvili**
► **A. Gharagyozyan**
Baghdad Open, 17.03.2017

1.+/-

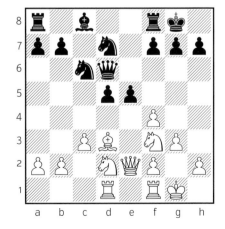

[57]

▷ **J. Glud**
► **M. Matthiesen**
Danish League, 19.03.2017

1.+-

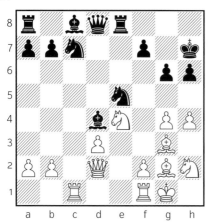

[58]

▷ **G. Antal**
► **R. Farkas**
Budapest Spring Open, 20.03.2017

1...−+

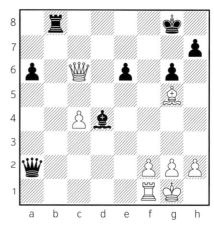

[59]

▷ **H. Odeev**
► **A. Timofeev**
Budapest Spring Open, 21.03.2017

1.+-

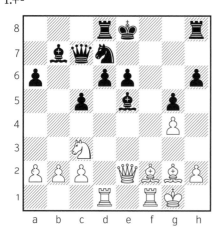

[60]

▷ **K. Stupak**
► **H. Odeev**
Budapest Spring Open, 22.03.2017

1.+-

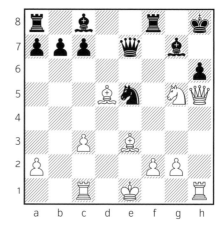

(61)

▷ **D. Sadzikowski**
► **A. Mista**
Polish Championship, 22.03.2017

1.+-

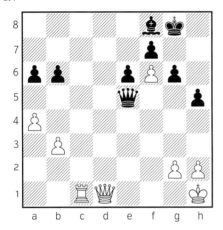

(62)

▷ **G. Papp**
► **L. Kessler**
Austrian League, 23.03.2017

1.+-

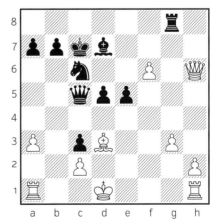

(63)

▷ **H. Wang**
► **S. Sethuraman**
Sharjah Masters, 25.03.2017

1.+-

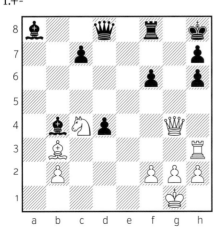

(64)

▷ **A. Tari**
► **A. Goganov**
Swedish League, 25.03.2017

1...−+

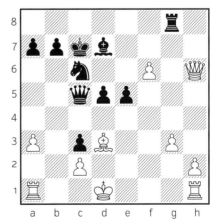

(65)

▷ A. Kveinys
► L. Stauskas
Baltic zt Vilnius, 25.03.2017

1.+-

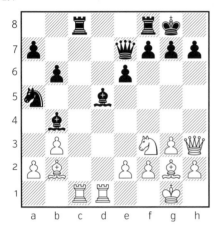

(66)

▷ K. Alekseenko
► E. Levin
St. Petersburg, 25.03.2017

1...-/+

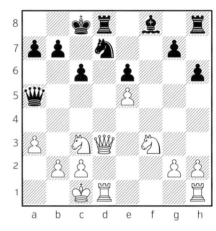

(67)

▷ E. Agrest
► H. Tikkanen
Swedish League, 25.03.2017

1.+-

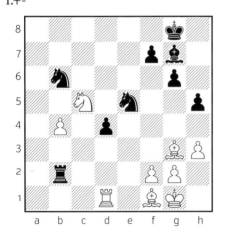

(68)

▷ V. Kovalev
► D. Popovic
Budapest Spring Open, 26.03.2017

1.+-

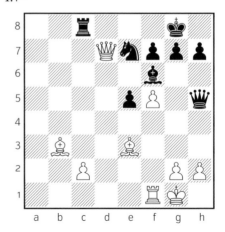

(69)

▷ **M. Manolache**
▶ **V. Nevednichy**
Romanian Championsip, 28.03.2017

1.+-

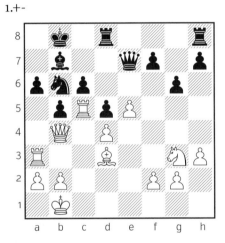

(70)

▷ **A. Kaliksteyn**
▶ **T. Ringoir**
Charlotte GM, 29.03.2017

1... -/+

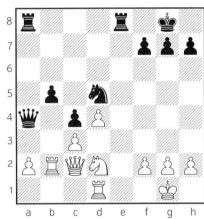

(71)

▷ **M. Bluebaum**
▶ **P. Vishnu**
Sharjah Masters, 29.03.2017

1. +/-

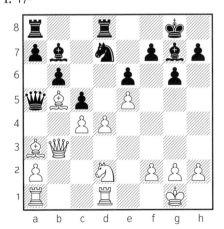

(72)

▷ **B. Adhiban**
▶ **H. Wang**
Sharjah Masters, 29.03.2017

1...−+

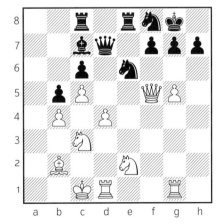

[73]

▷ A. Adly
► D. Anton Guijarro
Sharjah Masters, 31.03.2017

1.+-

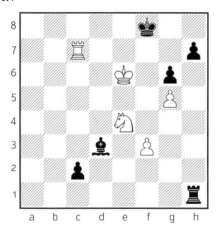

[74]

▷ L. Pantsulaia
► V. Raahul
Dubai Open, 04.04.2017

1.+-

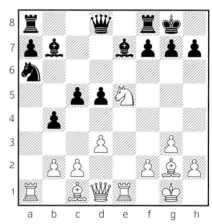

[75]

▷ F. Caruana
► G. Kamsky
American Championship, 04.04.2017

1.+-

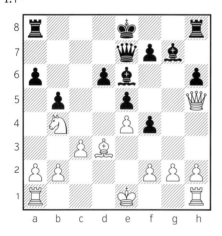

[76]

▷ V. Akobian
► F. Caruana
American Championship, 07.04.2017

1.+-

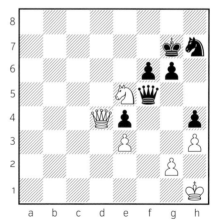

[77]

▷ **Y. Zherebukh**
▶ **H. Nakamura**
American Championship, 08.04.2017

1...–+

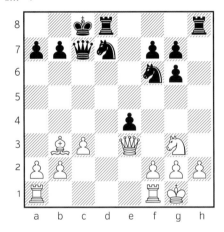

[78]

▷ **P. Stuemer**
▶ **G. Papp**
Karlsruhe Grenke Open, 13.04.2017

1...–+

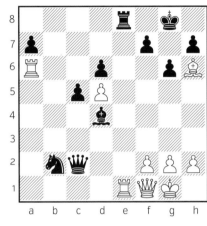

[79]

▷ **J. Guerra Mendez**
▶ **V. Baklan**
La Roda Open, 15.04.2017

1.+-

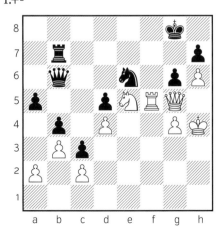

[80]

▷ **A. Demuth**
▶ **D. Nasshan**
Karlsruhe Grenke Open, 15.04.2017

1.+-

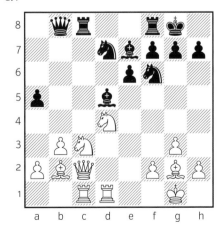

(81)

▷ **J. Blit**
► **D. Flores**
Mar del Plata Open, 15.04.2017

1.+-

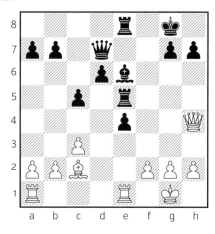

(82)

▷ **S. Martinovic**
► **L. Lodici**
Karlsruhe Grenke Open, 16.04.2017

1.+-

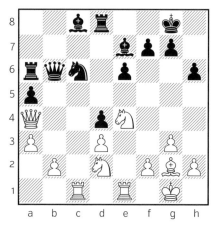

(83)

▷ **V. Kramnik**
► **P. Svidler**
Chess Challenge Blitz, 17.04.2017

1.+-

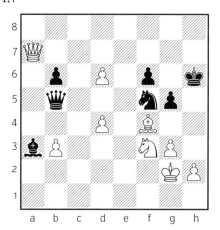

(84)

▷ **V. Anand**
► **B. Gelfand**
Chess Challenge Blitz, 17.04.2017

1.+-

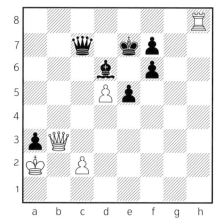

(85)

▷ D. Flores
► A. Bachmann
Szmetan Memorial, 20.04.2017

1.+-

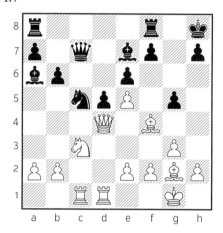

(86)

▷ E. Blomqvist
► A. Savage
Reykjavik Open, 22.04.2017

1.+-

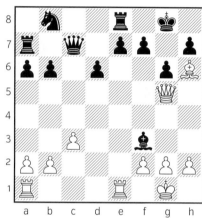

(87)

▷ Z. Almasi
► A. Ramirez
Reykjavik Open, 22.04.2017

1.+-

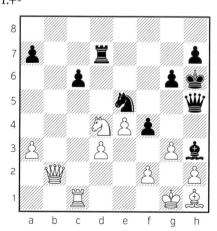

(88)

▷ H. Fuchs
► A. Graf
Bundesliga 2, 23.04.2017

1...−+

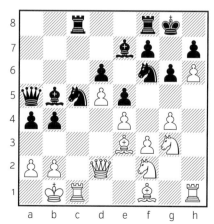

(89)

▷ J. Bai
► C. Wang
Chinese Championship, 23.04.2017

1...−+

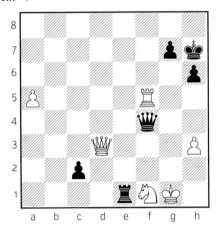

(90)

▷ B. Jobava
► K. Landa
Reykjavik Open, 24.04.2017

1.+−

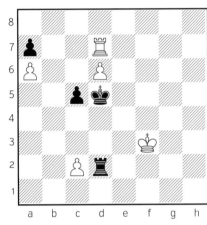

(91)

▷ A. Saric
► Z. Kozul
Croatian Championship, 26.04.2017

1...−+

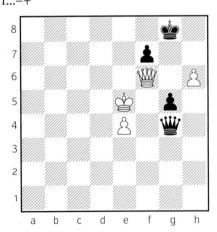

(92)

▷ M. Palac
► I. Saric
Croatian Championship, 26.04.2017

1...−+

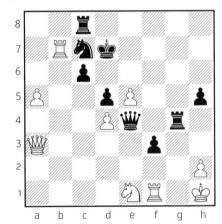

(93)

▷ **A. Huzman**
► **N. Short**
WC Seniors 50, 30.04.2017

1...−+

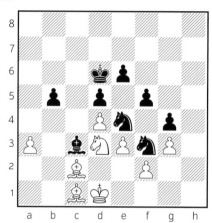

(94)

▷ **C. Bauer**
► **R. Stern**
Bundesliga, 30.04.2017

1.+−

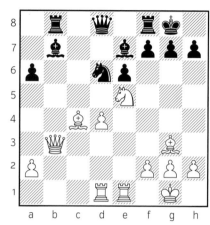

(95)

▷ **S. Bromberger**
► **J. Granda Zuniga**
Bundesliga, 01.05.2017

1.+−

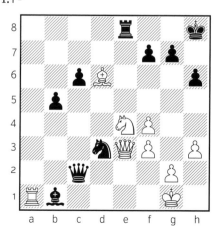

(96)

▷ **S. Saydaliev**
► **K. Stupak**
Agzamov Memorial, 04.05.2017

1...−+

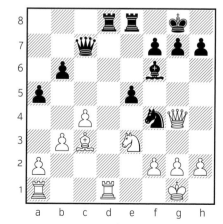

(97)

▷ **J. Stocek**
▶ **R. Biolek**
Czech Championship, 06.05.2017

1.+-

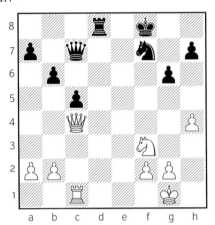

(98)

▷ **V. Babula**
▶ **P. Haba**
Czech Championship, 06.05.2017

1.+-

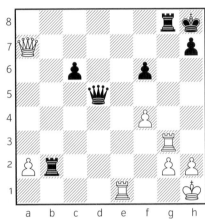

(99)

▷ **H. Asis Gargatagli**
▶ **M. Narciso Dublan**
Catalan League, 06.05.2017

1.+-

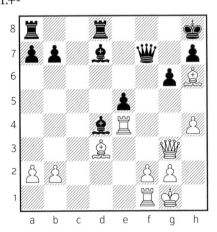

(100)

▷ **L. Fressinet**
▶ **E. Bacrot**
Balagna Rapid Open, 07.05.2017

1...−+

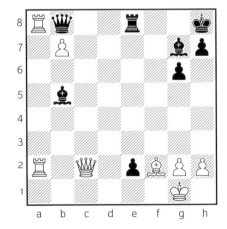

(101)

▷ **A. Shomoev**
► **G. Kamsky**
Russian League Sochi, 08.05.2017

1.+−

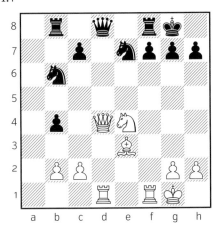

(102)

▷ **Y. Roshka**
► **S. Bogdanovich**
Lvov Rapid Cup, 08.05.2017

1...−+

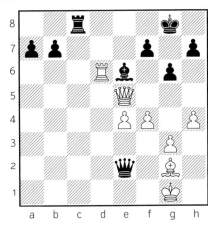

(103)

▷ **M. Oleksienko**
► **V. Bernadskiy**
Lvov Rapid Cup, 08.05.2017

1...−+

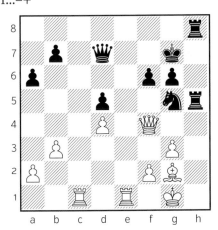

(104)

▷ **A. Giri**
► **E. Romanov**
Russian League Sochi, 08.05.2017

1.+−

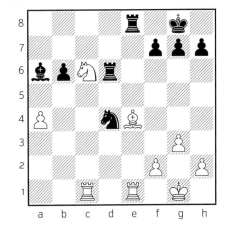

(105)

▷ R. Mamedov
► V. Onischuk
Lvov Rapid Cup, 09.05.2017

1...–+

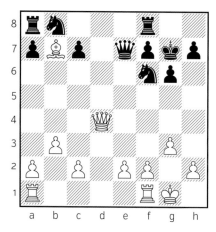

(106)

▷ M. Kazhgaleyev
► A. Urazayev
Agzamov Memorial, 09.05.2017

1.+-

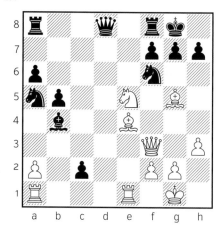

(107)

▷ S. Bogdanovich
► D. Kovalev
Lvov Rapid Cup, 09.05.2017

1.+-

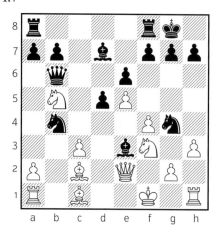

(108)

▷ A. Jankovic
► D. Raguz
Croatian Cup Mali Losinj, 11.05.2017

1.+-

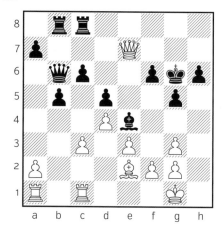

(109)

▷ **A. Brkic**
► **N. Sedlak**
Croatian Cup Mali Losinj, 11.05.2017

1...−+

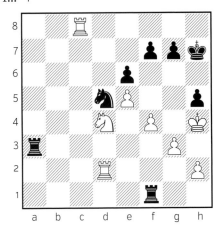

(110)

▷ **F. Urkedal**
► **D. Akdag**
Copenhagen Challenge, 13.05.2017

1.+−

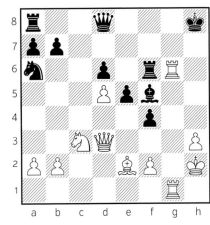

(111)

▷ **P. Harikrishna**
► **P. Svidler**
Fide GP Moscow, 14.05.2017

1...−+

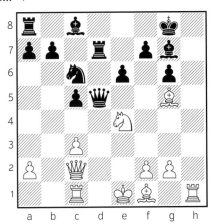

(112)

▷ **A. Goganov**
► **J. Ibanez Aullana**
Llucmajor Open, 14.05.2017

1.+−

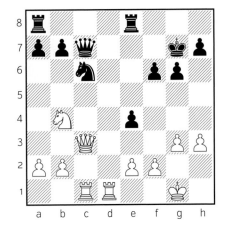

(113)

▷ A. Sokolov
► J. Moucheroud
French League, 19.05.2017

1. +/-

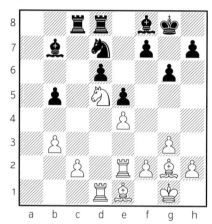

(114)

▷ M. Kanarek
► D. Mastrovasilis
Katowice Rapid, 20.05.2017

1...=

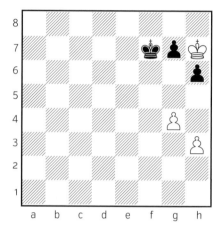

(115)

▷ X. Bu
► R. Jumabayev
Asian Continental Open, 20.05.2017

1.+-

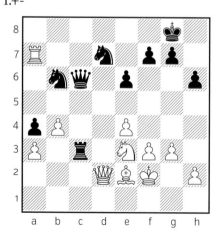

(116)

▷ T. Bueder
► K. Tarlev
Bodensee Open Bregenz, 21.05.2017

1.+-

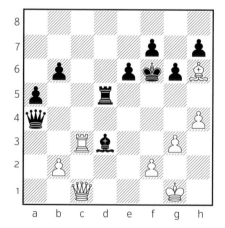

(117)

▷ S. Karjakin
► G. Meier
Internet Blitz, 24.05.2017

1.+-

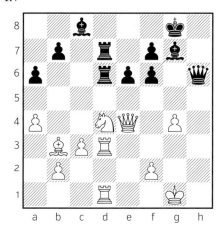

(118)

▷ S. Lu
► J. Bai
Chinese League, 25.05.2017

1.+-

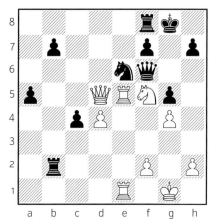

(119)

▷ N. Bueter
► V. Epishin
Stuttgart Open, 26.05.2017

1...-+

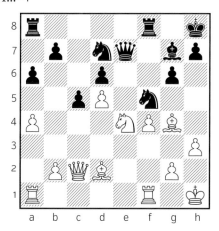

(120)

▷ P. Ponkratov
► I. Babikov
European Championship, 30.05.2017

1.+-

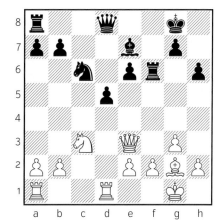

(121)

▷ S. Zhigalko
► A. Aleksandrov
European Championship, 02.06.2017

1. +/-

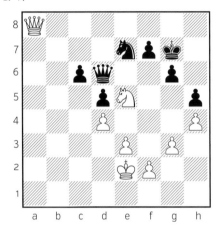

(122)

▷ D. Mastrovasilis
► A. Volokitin
European Championship, 02.06.2017

1.+-

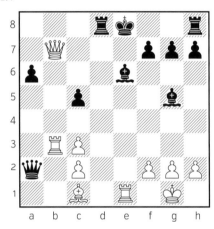

(123)

▷ T. Harutyunian
► S. Movsesian
European Championship, 02.06.2017

1.+-

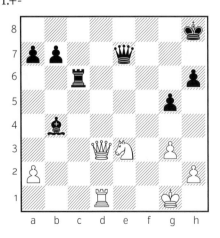

(124)

▷ D. Anton Guijarro
► O. Bortnyk
European Championship, 03.06.2017

1.+-

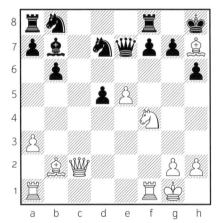

(125)

▷ **N. Heinichen**
► **A. Fier**
Maastricht Limburg Open, 04.06.2017

1...−+

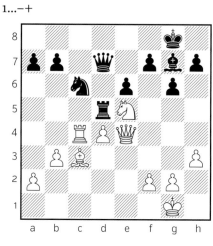

(126)

▷ **M. Jurcik**
► **S. Maze**
European Championship, 06.06.2017

1...−+

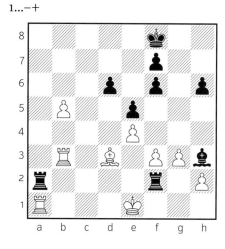

(127)

▷ **T. Gelashvili**
► **F. Berkes**
European Championship, 06.06.2017

1.+−

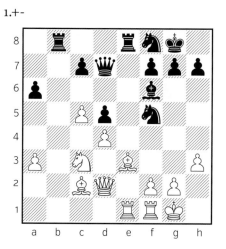

(128)

▷ **B. Jobava**
► **D. Mastrovasilis**
European Championship, 07.06.2017

1.+−

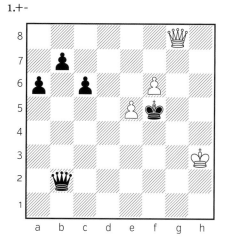

(129)

▷ G. Jones
► B. Jobava
European Championship, 08.06.2017

1...−+

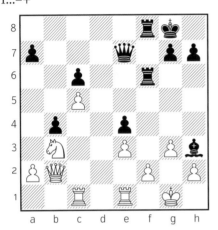

(130)

▷ C. Ali Marandi
► S. Bogdanovich
European Championship, 08.06.2017

1.+−

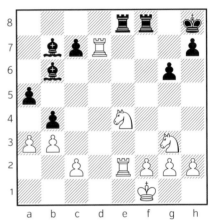

(131)

▷ F. Berkes
► J. Tomczak
European Championship, 10.06.2017

1...=

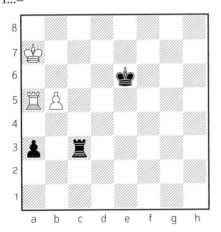

(132)

▷ Y. Yu
► X. Xu
Chinese League, 12.06.2017

1.+−

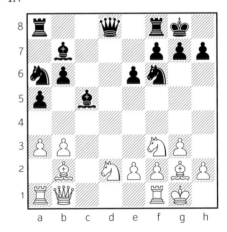

(133)

▷ C. Cruz
► H. Panesso Rivera
American Continental, 14.06.2017

1.+-

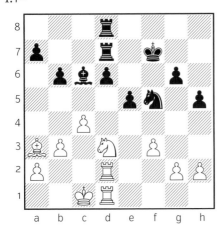

(134)

▷ S. Sevian
► R. Vasquez Schroder
American Continental, 15.06.2017

1.+-

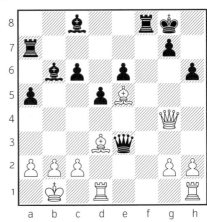

(135)

▷ C. Gokerkan
► V. Malakhatko
Cesme Open, 15.06.2017

1.+-

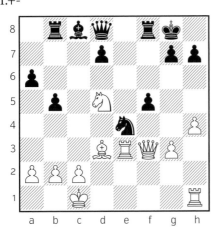

(136)

▷ R. Li
► A. He
Las Vegas National Open, 17.06.2017

1.+-

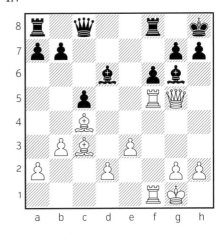

(137)

▷ V. Rasulov
► D. Magalashvili
Cesme Open, 18.06.2017

1.+-

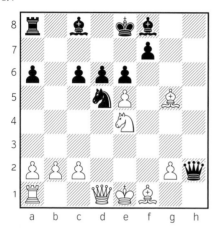

(138)

▷ A. Fier
► A. Ramirez
American Continental R, 18.06.2017

1.+-

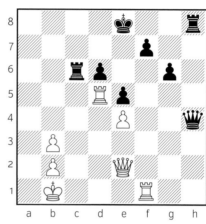

(139)

▷ K. Sasikiran
► R. Robson
World Team Champ., 20.06.2017

1.+-

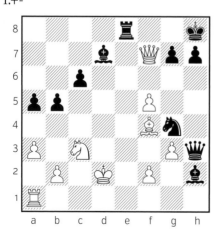

(140)

▷ K. Lagno
► L. Javakhishvili
World Team Champ., 20.06.2017

1.+-

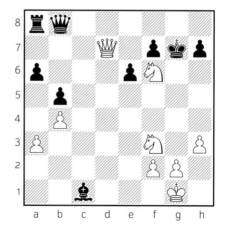

(141)

▷ O. Ladva
► A. Neiksans
Baltic zt Liepaja, 20.06.2017

1.+-

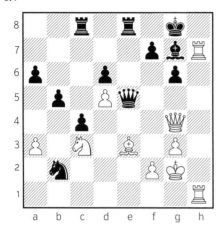

(142)

▷ S. Mamedyarov
► M. Carlsen
Paris GCT Rapid, 21.06.2017

1...−+

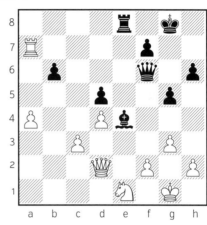

(143)

▷ I. Nepomniachtchi
► J. Duda
World Team Champ., 23.06.2017

1.+-

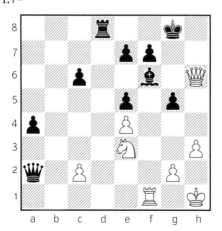

(144)

▷ A. Donchenko
► R. Frischmann
German Championship, 23.06.2017

1.+-

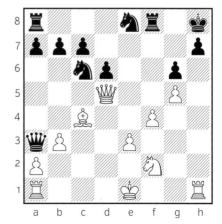

(145)

▷ W. So
► M. Carlsen
Paris GCT Blitz, 24.06.2017

1...–+

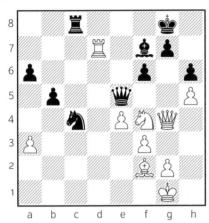

(146)

▷ G. Popilski
► Y. Zherebukh
NY International Open, 24.06.2017

1...–+

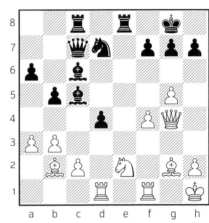

(147)

▷ S. Mamedyarov
► V. Topalov
Paris GCT Blitz, 25.06.2017

1.+–

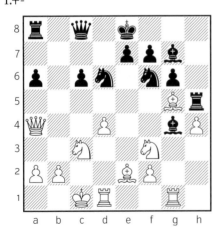

(148)

▷ B. Rogulj
► B. Kurajica
Karlovac, 27.06.2017

1.+–

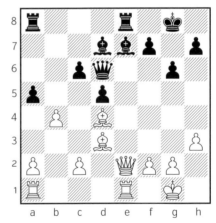

(149)

▷ M. Carlsen
► L. Aronian
Leuven GCT Blitz, 28.06.2017

1.+-

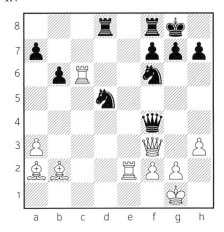

(150)

▷ S. Poormosavi
► P. Darini
Asia zt Teheran, 30.06.2017

1.+-

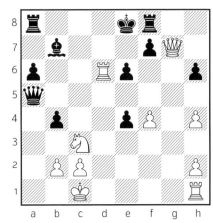

(151)

▷ E. Moradiabadi
► D. Aaron
Philadelphia World Open, 01.07.2017

1.+-

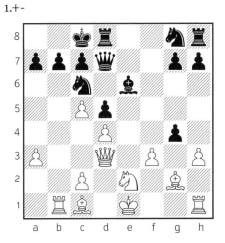

(152)

▷ M. Carlsen
► V. Ivanchuk
Leuven GCT Blitz, 01.07.2017

1.+-

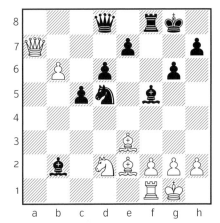

(153)

▷ **M. Krasenkow**
► **E. Safarli**
Porticcio Open, 02.07.2017

1.+-

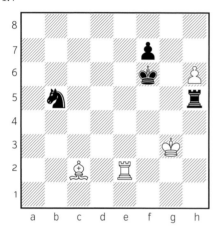

(154)

▷ **L. Aronian**
► **M. Vachier-Lagrave**
Leuven GCT Blitz, 02.07.2017

1...–+

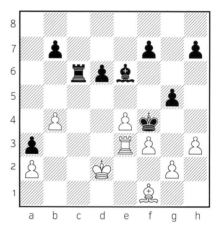

(155)

▷ **L. Aronian**
► **I. Nepomniachtchi**
Leuven GCT Blitz, 02.07.2017

1.+-

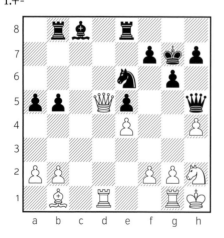

(156)

▷ **I. Rozum**
► **D. Khismatullin**
Russian Higher League, 03.07.2017

1.+-

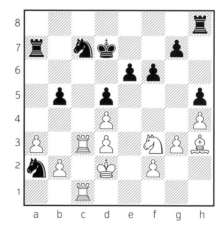

(157)

▷ V. Zvjaginsev
► M. Antipov
Russian Higher League, 04.07.2017

1.+-

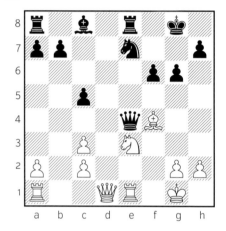

(158)

▷ P. Czarnota
► A. Istratescu
Greek League, 04.07.2017

1.+-

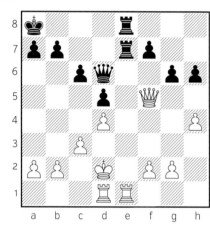

(159)

▷ A. Riazantsev
► P. Harikrishna
Geneva FIDE GP, 06.07.2017

1...-+

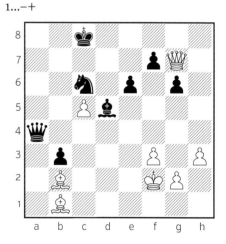

(160)

▷ O. Noroozi
► P. Darini
Asia zt Teheran, 06.07.2017

1.+-

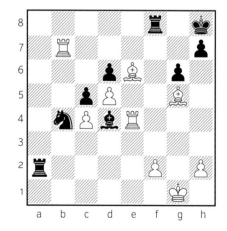

[161]

▷ **K. Grigoryan**
► **K. Ojas**
Barbera del Valles Open, 06.07.2017

1.+−

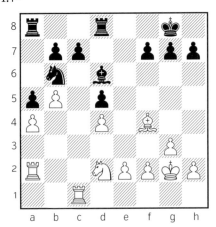

[162]

▷ **S. Mamedyarov**
► **E. Inarkiev**
Fide GP Geneva, 07.07.2017

1.+−

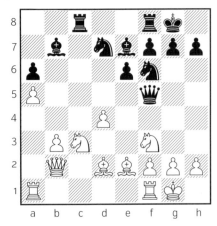

[163]

▷ **A. Konstantinov**
► **V. Sanal**
Paracin Summer Open, 07.07.2017

1...−+

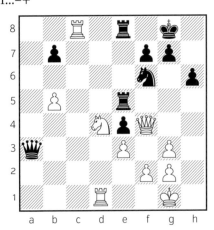

[164]

▷ **L. Trent**
► **N. Lubbe**
Lueneburg GM, 08.07.2017

1...−+

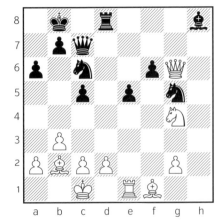

(165)

▷ **D. Sadzikowski**
► **A. David**
Greek League, 08.07.2017

1. +/-

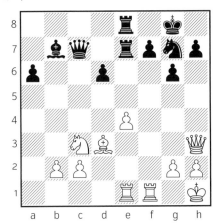

(166)

▷ **A. Kovacevic**
► **E. Tanriverdi**
Paracin Summer Open, 08.07.2017

1. +-

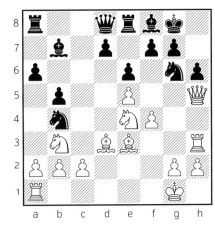

(167)

▷ **D. Kollars**
► **P. Keyser**
Lueneburg Open, 08.07.2017

1. +-

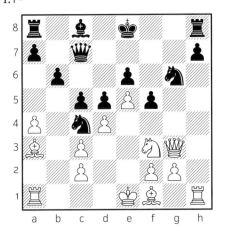

(168)

▷ **A. Gupta**
► **S. Vaibhav**
Commonwealth Champ., 08.07.2017

1. +-

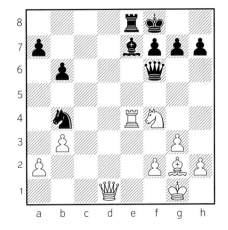

(169)

▷ T. Kantans
► P. Prohaszka
Benasque Open, 10.07.2017

1.+−

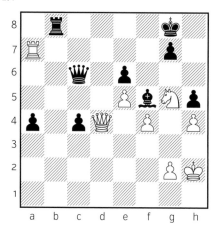

(170)

▷ S. Salem
► Y. Hou
Geneva FIDE GP, 12.07.2017

1...−+

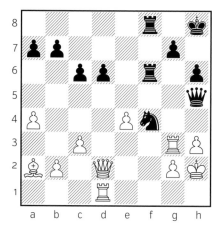

(171)

▷ D. Vocaturo
► P. Prohaszka
Benasque Open, 13.07.2017

1...−+

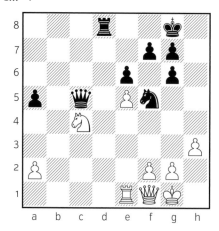

(172)

▷ J. Soyer
► N. Maiorov
Vaujany Open, 13.07.2017

1...−+

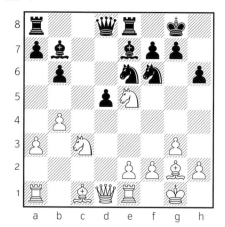

(173)

▷ **A. Kovacevic**
► **I. Can**
Paracin Summer Open, 14.07.2017

1...–+

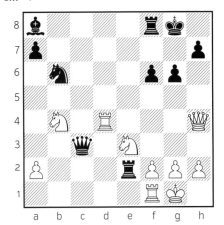

(174)

▷ **A. Mokshanov**
► **V. Belous**
Samara Polugaevsky Mem, 15.07.2017

1...–+

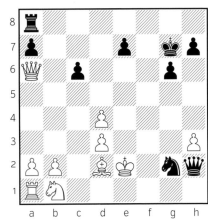

(175)

▷ **D. Derakhshani**
► **F. Rambaldi**
Bergamo Open, 15.07.2017

1...–+

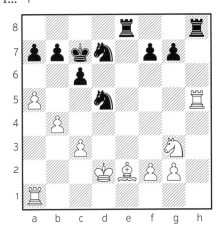

(176)

▷ **A. Naiditsch**
► **R. Ponomariov**
Danzhou, 17.07.2017

1.+–

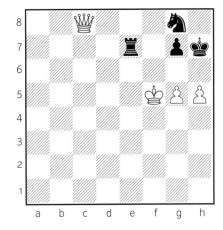

(177)

▷ V. Georgiev
► S. Gauri
Dayton Masters, 18.07.2017

1.+-

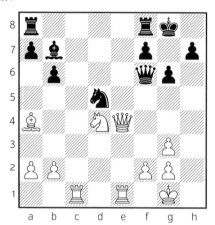

(178)

▷ P. Schlosser
► R. Vogel
Pardubice Open Rapid, 20.07.2017

1...−+

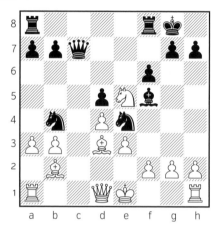

(179)

▷ S. Dvoirys
► M. Manik
Pardubice Open, 20.07.2017

1...−+

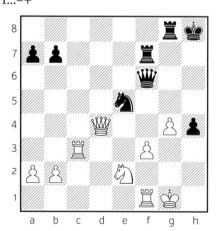

(180)

▷ M. Parligras
► A. Demchenko
Turkish League, 21.07.2017

1.+-

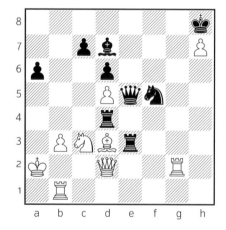

(181)

▷ **G. Gopal**
▶ **J. Vykouk**
Pardubice Open, 23.07.2017

1.+−

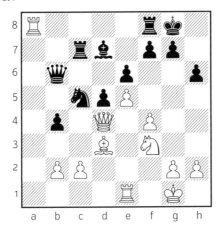

(182)

▷ **D. Forcen Esteban**
▶ **I. Akash Pc**
Andorra Open, 26.07.2017

1.+−

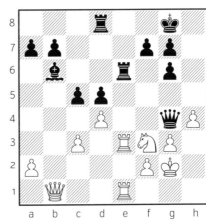

(183)

▷ **B. Dauth**
▶ **J. Schroeder**
Helsingor Xtracon Open, 26.07.2017

1.+−

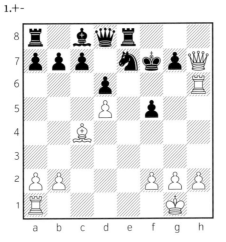

(184)

▷ **A. Seyb**
▶ **M. Antipov**
Biel MTO Open, 27.07.2017

1...−+

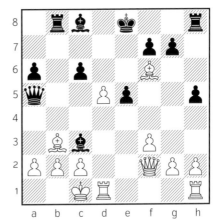

(185)

▷ B. Juhasz
► M. Stojanovic
Senta Open, 27.07.2017

1...–+

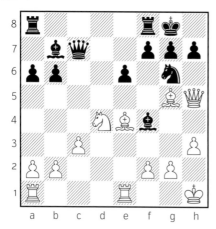

(186)

▷ Y. Wen
► X. Xu
Chinese League, 28.07.2017

1... –/+

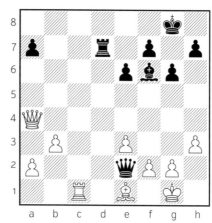

(187)

▷ A. Kvon
► F. Svane
Helsingor Xtracon Open, 29.07.2017

1.+-

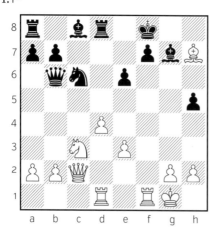

(188)

▷ M. Kravtsiv
► I. Rozum
Turkish League, 30.07.2017

1.+-

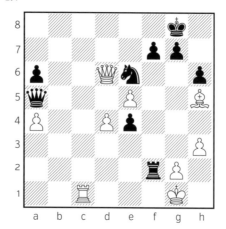

(189)

▷ **Y. Hou**
► **E. Bacrot**
Biel GM, 31.07.2017

1.+-

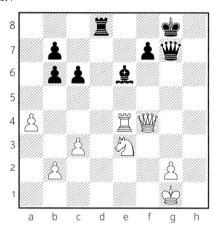

(190)

▷ **V. Dragnev**
► **P. Vishnu**
Biel MTO Open, 01.08.2017

1...−+

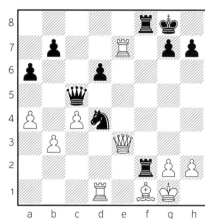

(191)

▷ **P. Harikrishna**
► **E. Bacrot**
Biel GM, 02.08.2017

1...−+

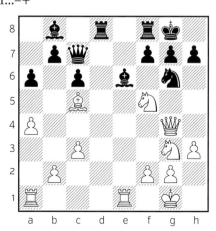

(192)

▷ **L. Aronian**
► **F. Caruana**
Sinquefield Cup, 03.08.2017

1...−+

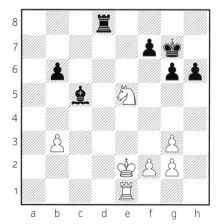

(193)

▷ M. Kravtsiv
► S. Zhigalko
Turkish League, 04.08.2017

1.+-

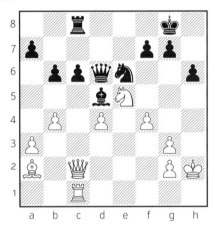

(194)

▷ N. Grandelius
► D. Yuffa
Lund CellaVision Cup, 06.08.2017

1.+-

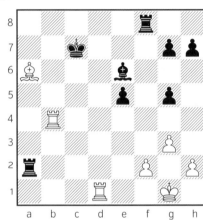

(195)

▷ J. Ehlvest
► A. Neiksans
Liepajas Rokade Rapid, 06.08.2017

1...−+

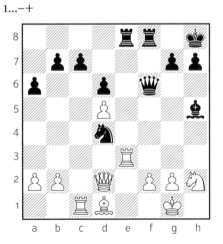

(196)

▷ V. Jianu
► C. Voiteanu
Arad Open, 07.08.2017

1.+-

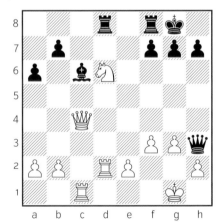

(197)

▷ P. Salinas Herrera
► K. Grigoryan
Badalona Open, 09.08.2017

1...−+

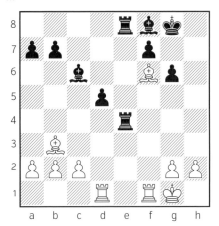

(198)

▷ D. Miedema
► D. Kryakvin
Riga Tech Open, 09.08.2017

1...−+

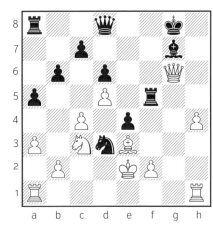

(199)

▷ Ali C. Marandi
► T. Kaasen
Riga Tech Open, 11.08.2017

1.+−

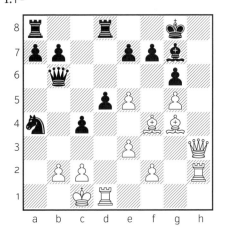

(200)

▷ D. Alsina Leal
► F. Podvin
Spanish Championship R, 13.08.2017

1...−+

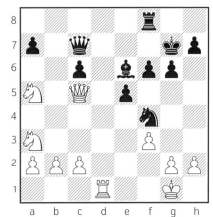

(201)

▷ **A. Alonso Rosell**
► **F. Garcia Molina**
Spanish Championship R, 13.08.2017

1.+-

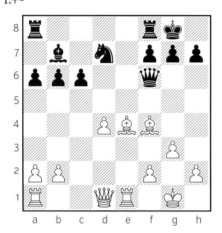

(202)

▷ **Q. Le**
► **F. Caruana**
Saint Louis Rapid, 14.08.2017

1...−+

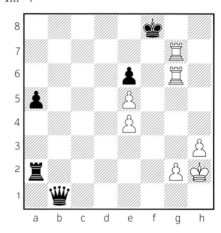

(203)

▷ **A. Indjic**
► **L. Vogt**
Abu Dhabi Open, 15.08.2017

1.+-

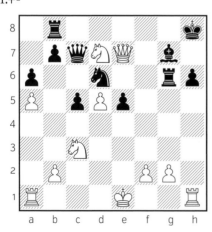

(204)

▷ **A. Leniart**
► **M. Bartel**
Warakomska Memorial, 16.08.2017

1.+-

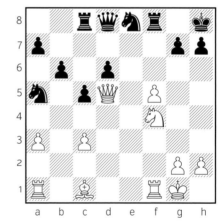

(205)

▷ S. Karjakin
► V. Anand
Saint Louis Rapid, 16.08.2017

1.+-

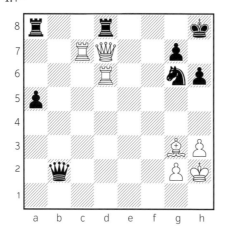

(206)

▷ N. Grandelius
► D. Forcen Esteban
Spanish League, 17.08.2017

1.+-

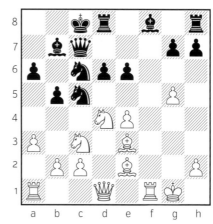

(207)

▷ H. Nakamura
► V. Anand
Saint Louis Blitz, 18.08.2017

1.+-

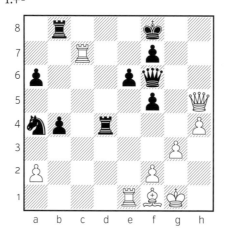

(208)

▷ J. Maia
► L. Krysa
Barcelona Sants Open, 18.08.2017

1...-+

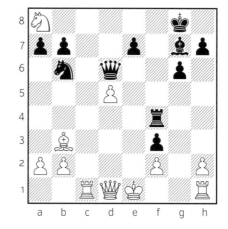

(209)

▷ C. Li
► Q. Ma
Chinese League, 18.08.2017

1.+-

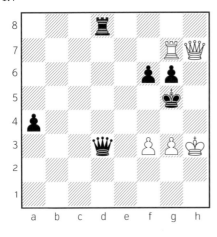

(210)

▷ A. Tahay
► L. Krysa
Barcelona Sants Open, 20.08.2017

1...−+

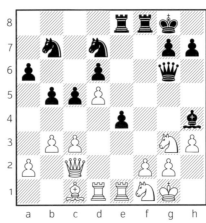

(211)

▷ E. Blomqvist
► M. Kleinman
Barcelona Sants Open, 20.08.2017

1...−+

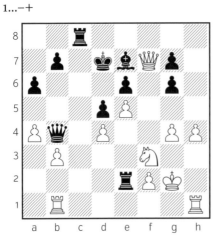

(212)

▷ I. Rozum
► D. Harika
Abu Dhabi Open, 21.08.2017

1.+-

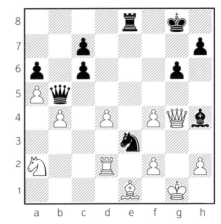

(213)

▷ **A. Stukopin**
► **B. Macieja**
US Masters Open, 25.08.2017

1. +/-

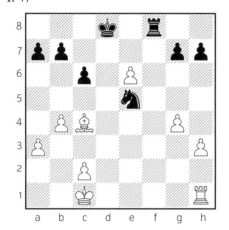

(214)

▷ **T. Kotanjian**
► **V. Teterev**
Avicenna Open Hamedan, 27.08.2017

1...−+

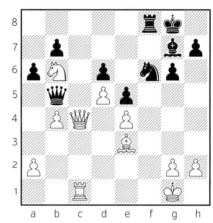

(215)

▷ **V. Artemiev**
► **D. Lintchevski**
St. Petersburg Rapid, 27.08.2017

1.+-

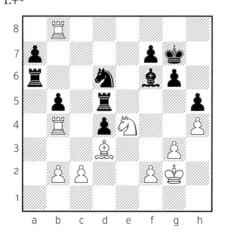

(216)

▷ **J. Xiong**
► **M. Vachier-Lagrave**
Internet Blitz, 30.08.2017

1...−+

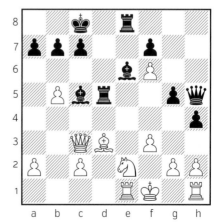

(217)

▷ **K. Shevchenko**
► **A. Barp**
Trieste Open, 02.09.2017

1...−+

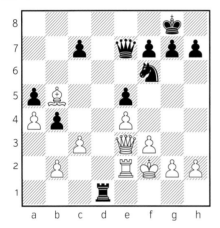

(218)

▷ **R. Markus**
► **D. Milanovic**
Serbian League, 03.09.2017

1.+-

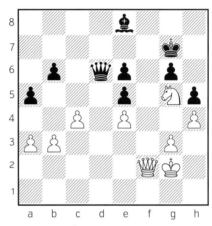

(219)

▷ **V. Dobrov**
► **A. Reshetnikov**
Moscow Blitz, 03.09.2017

1.+-

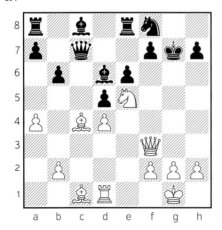

(220)

▷ **A. Dreev**
► **A. Bachmann**
Fide World Cup Tbilisi, 04.09.2017

1.+-

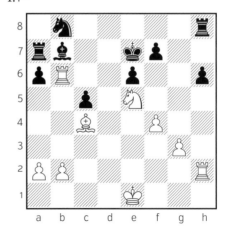

(221)

▷ **Y. Wei**
▶ **B. Sambuev**
Fide World Cup Tbilisi, 05.09.2017

1.+-

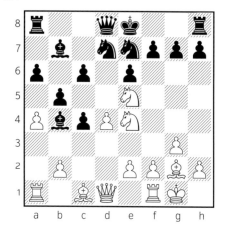

(222)

▷ **L. Lenic**
▶ **L. Fressinet**
Fide World Cup Tbilisi, 05.09.2017

1.+-

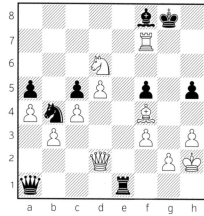

(223)

▷ **P. Harikrishna**
▶ **Y. Gonzalez Vidal**
Fide World Cup Tbilisi, 05.09.2017

1.+-

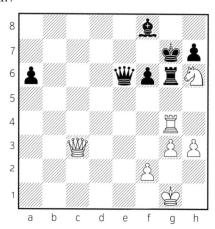

(224)

▷ **M. Adams**
▶ **T. Batchuluun**
Fide World Cup Tbilisi, 05.09.2017

1.+-

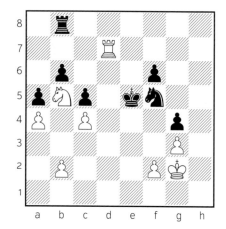

(225)

▷ W. So
► M. Bluebaum

FIDE World Cup Tbilisi, 08.09.2017

1.+-

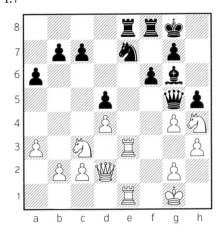

(226)

▷ D. Khegay
► I. Bocharov

Kurnosov Memorial Rapid, 09.09.2017

1...−+

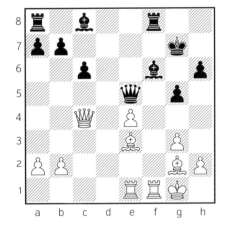

(227)

▷ B. Vuckovic
► S. Rogac

Serbian League, 10.09.2017

1.+-

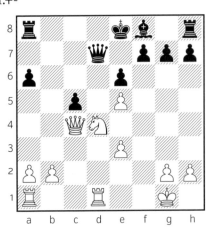

(228)

▷ I. Lysyj
► A. Shariyazdanov

Kurnosov Memorial Rapid, 10.09.2017

1.+-

(229)

▷ **D. Dubov**
► **V. Artemiev**
Fide World Cup Tbilisi, 10.09.2017

1.+-

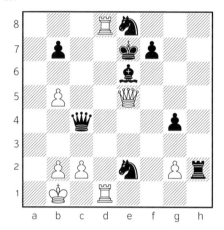

(230)

▷ **A. Arribas Lopez**
► **A. Pichot**
Saint Louis Fall-B, 10.09.2017

1...−+

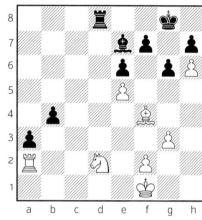

(231)

▷ **G. Meier**
► **V. Kovalev**
Saint Louis Fall-A, 11.09.2017

1.+-

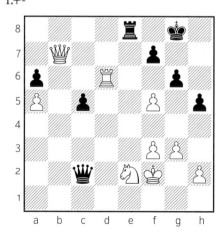

(232)

▷ **A. Lenderman**
► **M. Vachier-Lagrave**
Fide World Cup Tbilisi, 11.09.2017

1...−+

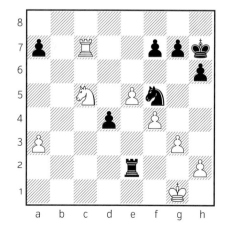

(233)

▷ B. Jobava
► I. Nepomniachtchi
Fide World Cup Tbilisi, 11.09.2017

1.+-

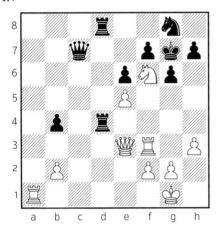

(234)

▷ M. Santos Ruiz
► A. Sousa
EU Championship U18, 14.09.2017

1.+-

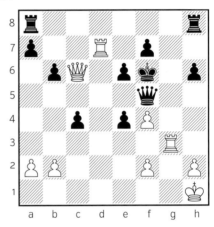

(235)

▷ A. Kislinsky
► M. Bagheri
Yerevan Open, 20.09.2017

1.+-

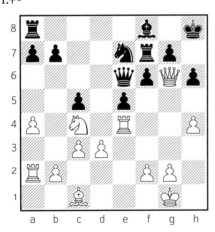

(236)

▷ D. Shengelia
► B. Bellahcene
Mitropa Cup, 25.09.2017

1...−+

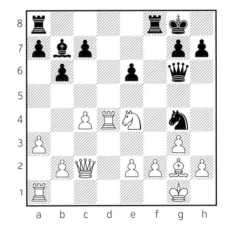

(237)

▷ Q. Le
► Y. Wang
Asian Team Champ. Rapid, 25.09.2017

1.+-

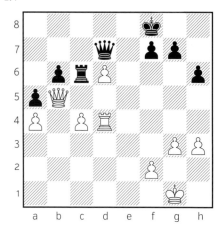

(238)

▷ R. Hovhannishyan
► A. Moskalenko
Yerevan Open, 25.09.2017

1.+-

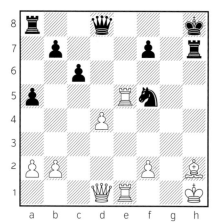

(239)

▷ R. Hovhannishyan
► M. Tabatabaei
Yerevan Open, 27.09.2017

1...−+

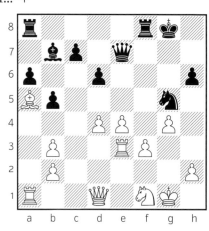

(240)

▷ L. Ding
► L. Aronian
Fide World Cup Tbilisi, 27.09.2017

1...−+

(241)

▷ A. Jakubiec
► M. Krasenkow
Polish League, 29.09.2017

1...–+

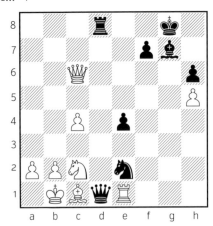

(242)

▷ I. Sokolov
► R. Rapport
Douglas IoM Open, 30.09.2017

1...–+

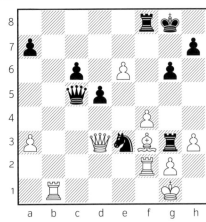

(243)

▷ D. Howell
► J. Timman
Douglas IoM Open, 30.09.2017

1.+-

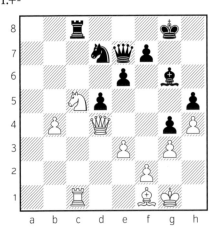

(244)

▷ Z. Tsydypov
► A. Sorokin
Russian Championship R, 01.10.2017

1.+-

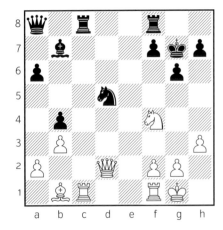

(245)

▷ **V. Anand**
► **Y. Hou**
Douglas IoM Open, 01.10.2017

1. +/-

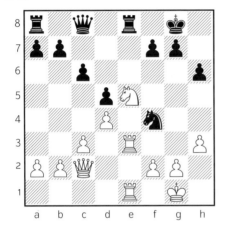

(246)

▷ **M. Demidov**
► **A. Korotylev**
Russian Champ. Blitz, 02.10.2017

1. +/-

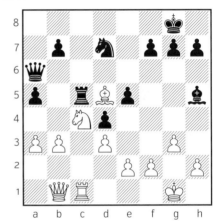

(247)

▷ **O. Girya**
► **E. Ovod**
Russian League Rapid, 03.10.2017

1.+-

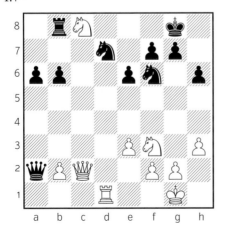

(248)

▷ **S. Feller**
► **Z. Medvegy**
Croatian League, 03.10.2017

1.+-

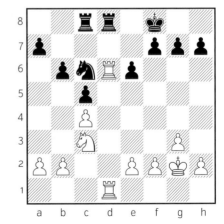

(249)

▷ **V. Artemiev**
► **A. Morozevich**
Russian League Rapid, 04.10.2017

1.+-

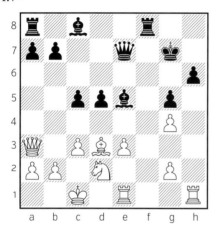

(250)

▷ **M. Lagarde**
► **V. Fedoseev**
EU Club Cup Antalya, 09.10.2017

1...–+

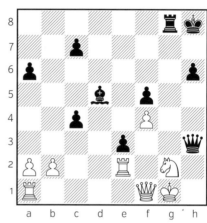

(251)

▷ **H. Steingrimsson**
► **Z. Efimenko**
EU Club Cup Antalya, 10.10.2017

1...–+

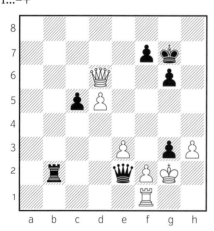

(252)

▷ **A. Naiditsch**
► **V. Kramnik**
EU Club Cup Antalya, 12.10.2017

1.+-

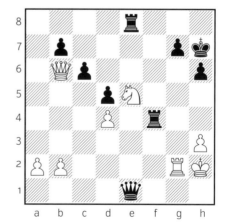

(253)

▷ C. Li
► L. Shytaj
French League, 22.10.2017

1.+-

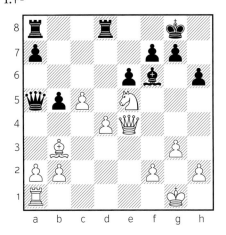

(254)

▷ N. Dzagnidze
► O. Girya
EU Championship Rapid, 22.10.2017

1...−+

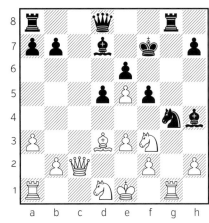

(255)

▷ V. Gunina
► A. Kosteniuk
EU Championship Blitz, 23.10.2017

1...−+

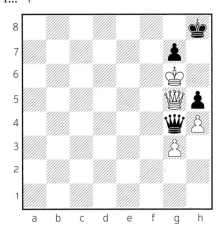

(256)

▷ P. Tregubov
► J. Moussard
Corsica Masters Bastia R, 26.10.2017

1...−+

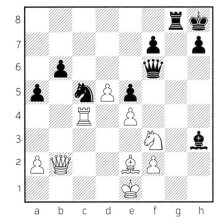

(257)

▷ **V. Onischuk**
► **A. Puranik**
Corsica Masters Op. Bastia, 26.10.2017

1.+-

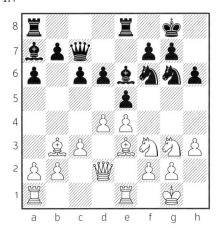

(258)

▷ **C. Repka**
► **M. Bartel**
EU Team Championship, 28.10.2017

1.+-

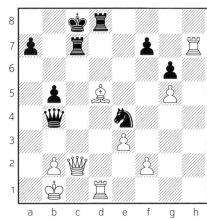

(259)

▷ **D. Navara**
► **A. Rasmussen**
EU Team Championship, 28.10.2017

1.+-

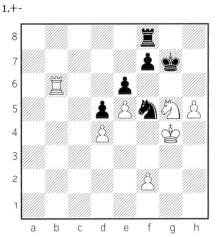

(260)

▷ **A. Giri**
► **P. Eljanov**
EU Team Championship, 29.10.2017

1.+-

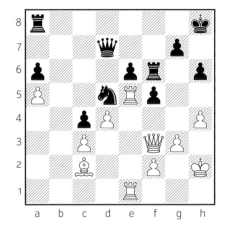

(261)

▷ V. Artemiev
▶ A. Sarana
Chigorin Memorial, 29.10.2017

1...−+

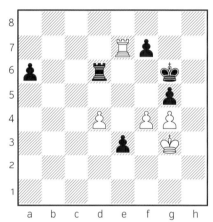

(262)

▷ L. Paichadze
▶ G. Kjartansson
EU Team Championship, 30.10.2017

1.+−

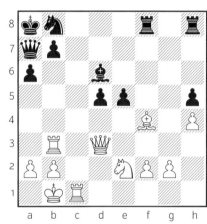

(263)

▷ A. Fedorov
▶ J. Skoberne
EU Team Championship, 30.10.2017

1.+−

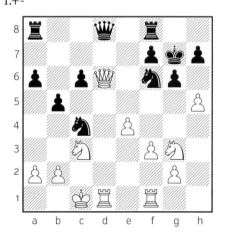

(264)

▷ S. Mamedyarov
▶ D. Svetushkin
EU Team Championship, 31.10.2017

1.+−

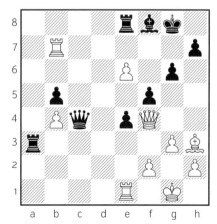

(265)

▷ A. Demuth
► A. Savina

Karpov Trophy Blitz, 31.10.2017

1.+-

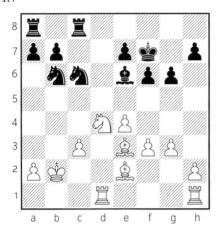

(266)

▷ G. Kjartansson
► M. Sebenik

EU Team Championship, 01.11.2017

1...−+

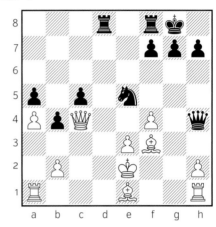

(267)

▷ A. Demuth
► A. Pourramezanali

Karpov Trophy Rapid, 01.11.2017

+-

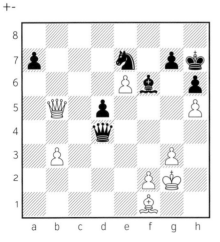

(268)

▷ C. Aravindh
► S. Swapnil

Indian Championship, 01.11.2017

1.+-

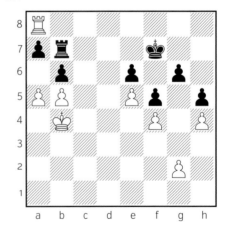

(269)

▷ **Z. Almasi**
► **H. Stevic**
EU Team Championship, 03.11.2017

1.+-

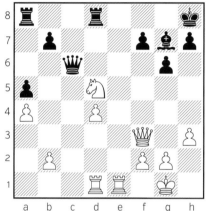

(270)

▷ **A. Ramirez**
► **A. Alvarez Pedraza**
Chess Rumble Rapid, 04.11.2017

1.+-

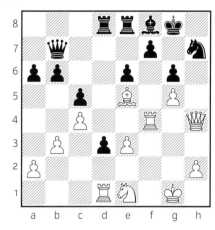

(271)

▷ **A. Ushenina**
► **A. Matnadze**
EU Team Championship, 05.11.2017

1...−+

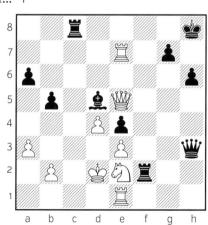

(272)

▷ **I. Salgado Lopez**
► **M. Mchedlishvili**
EU Team Championship, 05.11.2017

1.+-

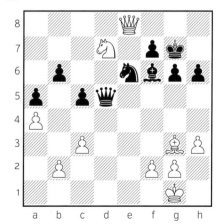

(273)

▷ H. Gabuzyan
► N. Sedlak
EU Team Championship, 06.11.2017

1...−+

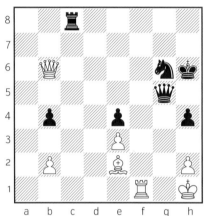

(274)

▷ S. Bogner
► S. Brunello
EU Team Championship, 06.11.2017

1.+-

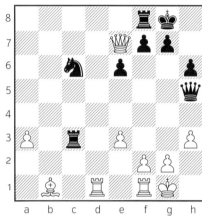

(275)

▷ D. Fridman
► S. Ernst
Bundesliga, 12.11.2017

1. +/-

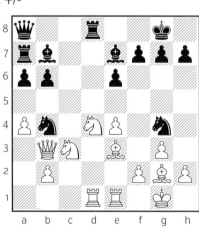

(276)

▷ S. Bromberger
► A. Horvath
Bundesliga, 12.11.2017

1...−+

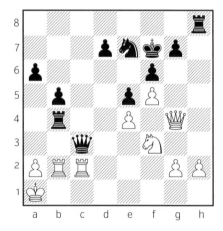

(277)

▷ I. Barreto
▶ D. Lima
Duchamp Open, 17.11.2017

1...−+

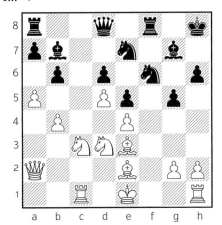

(278)

▷ W. So
▶ M. Carlsen
Internet Blitz, 18.11.2017

1.+-

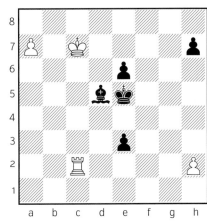

(279)

▷ W. So
▶ M. Carlsen
Internet Blitz, 18.11.2017

1...−+

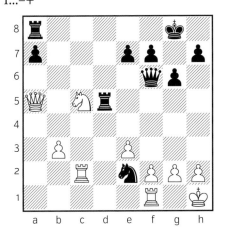

(280)

▷ A. Kveinys
▶ B. Amin
Latvian League, 18.11.2017

1...−+

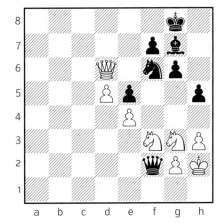

(281)

▷ J. Sadorra
► A. Hambleton
St Louis GM Invitational, 19.11.2017

1.=

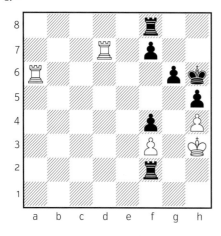

(282)

▷ L. Aronian
► A. Giri
Palma De Mallorca GP, 19.11.2017

1.+-

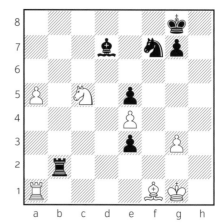

(283)

▷ E. Tomashevsky
► T. Radjabov
Palma De Mallorca GP, 22.11.2017

1.+-

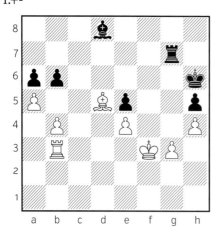

(284)

▷ A. Riazantsev
► R. Rapport
Palma De Mallorca GP, 22.11.2017

1...−+

(285)

▷ **D. Bocharov**
► **D. Kokarev**
Ugra Governor's Cup Blitz, 22.11.2017

1.+−

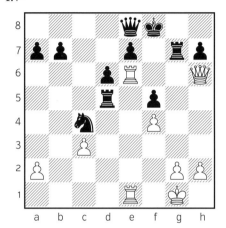

(286)

▷ **P. Eljanov**
► **J. Hammer**
Palma De Mallorca GP, 23.11.2017

1.+−

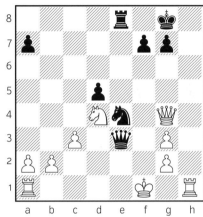

(287)

▷ **A. Gilevych**
► **A. Stella**
Italian Championship, 29.11.2017

1...−+

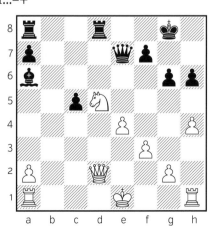

(288)

▷ **M. Bosiocic**
► **S. Shyam**
Tsaghkadzor Open, 01.12.2017

1...−+

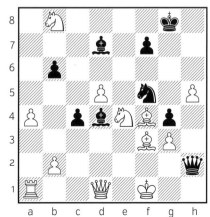

(289)

▷ **S. Maze**
► **G. Stany**
London Classic Open, 08.12.2017

1.+-

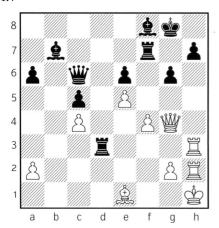

(290)

▷ **A. Graf**
► **V. Babula**
Bundesliga, 10.12.2017

1...−+

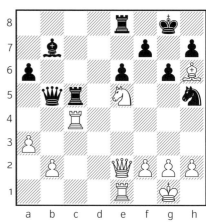

(291)

▷ **D. Dvirnyy**
► **S. Brunello**
Italian Championship, 10.12.2017

1...−+

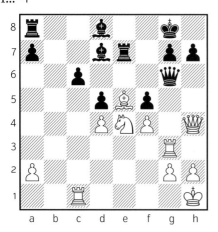

(292)

▷ **M. Carlsen**
► **I. Nepomniachtchi**
London Classic, 10.12.2017

1...−+

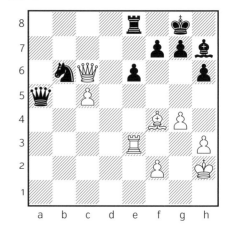

(293)

▷ **K. Grigoryan**
► **N. Norbaev**
Johor Open, 12.12.2017

1.+-

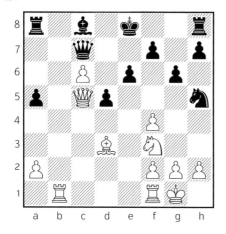

(294)

▷ **A. Krstulovic**
► **V. Malakhatko**
Zadar Open Blitz, 13.12.2017

1...−+

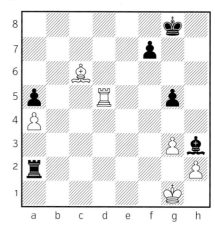

(295)

▷ **B. Gledura**
► **A. Indjic**
Hetenyi Geza Memorial GM, 15.12.2017

1.+-

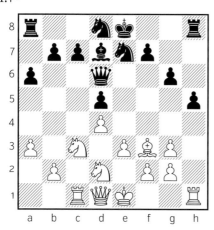

(296)

▷ **A. Horvath**
► **I. Leventic**
Hungarian League, 17.12.2017

1.+-

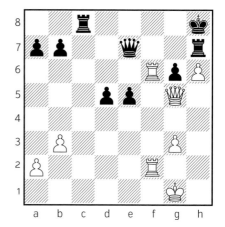

[297]

▷ O. Almeida Quintana
► A. Gorovets
Carlos Torre Memorial, 17.12.2017

1.+-

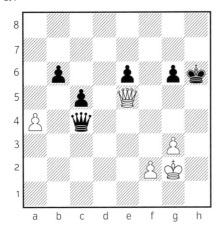

[298]

▷ S. Nihal
► R. Zhalmakhanov
World Youth U16 Olympiad, 18.12.2017

1.+-

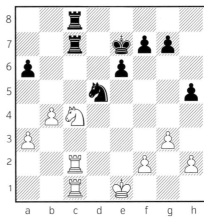

[299]

▷ Z. Medvegy
► T. Banusz
Hetenyi Geza Memorial GM, 20.12.2017

1... -/+

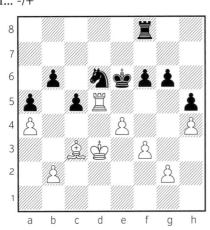

[300]

▷ S. Mamedyarov
► D. Yuffa
Nutcracker Classical, 21.12.2017

1.+-

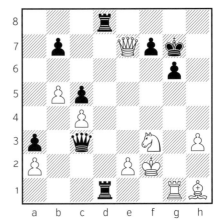

– SOLUTIONS –

(1)

▷ U. Kersten
► S. Fedorchuk
Staufer Open, 02.01.2017

11.c4! ♗xc4 12. ♗xc4 [12.♕a4+? b5∓]
12...♕xc4 13.♖c1 1–0

(2)

▷ A. Heimann
► B. Stillger
Basel Open, 04.01.2017

25.♖e4! 1–0[25.♖e4 ♖xe4 (25...♖cd8
26.♖xc4+-) 26.♘xe4 ♔e6 27.♖xc4
♔d5 28.♘d2+-]

(3)

▷ D. Svetushkin
► D. Forcen Esteban
Roquetas de Mar Open, 05.01.2017

44.♔a7! a2 45.♔b8 ♖b2 46.♖a6
e5 [46...♔d7 47.♔a8 ♔c7 48.♖a7+-]
47.fxe5 +-

(4)

▷ E. Safarli
► A. Donchenko
Basel Open, 05.01.2017

17.♘f6+! ♔h8 18.♘h5 ♖g8 [18...g6
19.♕e5+ f6 20.♕xf6++-] 19.♖d8!!
1–0 [19.♖d8 ♖xd8 20.♕xg7#]

(5)

▷ R. Kevlishvili
► C. Bauer
Basel Open, 05.01.2017

20...♘e2+! 21.♔b1 ♕c4 22.♗b3
♕xe4 23.♗xe6 ♘xc3+ 24.bxc3 fxe6
0–1

(6)

▷ M. Antipov
► S. Ivanov
Rilton Cup Stockholm, 05.01.2017

31.♕xf8+! ♔xf8 32.♘g5+ ♗xf1 [32...
♕f5 33.♘xh7+ ♔e7 34.♖xf5 gxf5
35.♔f2+-] 33.♘xe6+ ♔e7 34.♔xf1
♔xe6 35.c6 1–0

(7)

▷ J. Hammer
► R. Elseth
Norwegian Championship Blitz
Sandefjord, 06.01.2017

14.♘xd5! cxd5 [14...♕e6 15.♘f4 ♕f6
16.♕d2 ♗xe5 17.dxe5 ♕xe5 18.♖ac1±]
15.♗xd5 ♗xe5 16.dxe5 ♕xe5
17.♗xa8 ♗xe2 18.♖e1 ♖e8 19.♕d2
♘a6 20.♗f3 1–0

(8)

▷ K. Piorun
▶ W. Przybylski
Polish Championship Rapid Zgierz,
08.01.2017

17.♗xh6! b5 [17...gxh6 18.♕g6+ ♔h8
19.♕xh6+ ♔g8 20.♖e4+–] 18.♘g5
♘f6 19.♕g6! ♗xh2+ 20.♔h1 1–0

(9)

▷ S. Gajewski
▶ B. Socko
Polish Championship Rapid Zgierz,
08.01.2017

48...♘e5! 49.♕f4 [49.♘xe5 ♖e1+–+]
49...♖e1+ 50.♘xe1 ♕xf4 0–1

(10)

▷ L. Dek
▶ G. Meier
Internet Pro League Rapid,
11.01.2017

22...♖xc2! 23.♖xc2 ♖xd1+ 24.♘e1
♖xe1# 0–1

(11)

▷ H. Gabuzyan
▶ S. Ter Sahakyan
Armenian League Yerevan,
16.01.2017

32...f3+! 33.♕xf3 [33.♖xf3 ♕xg4+
34.♔h2 ♖xf3–+] 33...♖xf3 34.♖xf3
♕xg4+ 35.♖g3 ♕e2+ 36.♔h3 ♕xc2
37.♖f1 ♕xd3 0–1

(12)

▷ S. Mareco
▶ M. Leskovar
Internet Pro League Rapid,
18.01.2017

23.♘xc6! ♗xc6 24.♗xd5 exd5
25.♕e6+ ♕f7 26.♖xc6 1–0

(13)

▷ R. Jumabayev
▶ A. Yatzenko
Internet Pro League Rapid,
18.01.2017

26...♕a7+! 0–1

(14)

▷ S. Lu
▶ J. Van Foreest
Wijk aan Zee, 20.01.2017

18.♗xg7!! ♔xg7 19.f6+! ♘xf6
[19...♗xf6 20.♘f5+ ♔f8 21.♕h5+–
] 20.♘f5+ ♔h7 21.♘xe7 ♕xe7
22.♕xf6 ♕xf6 23.♖xf6 ♔g7 24.♖af1
♘d8 25.♖6f2 ♖e7 26.♘xd5 +–

(15)

▷ E. Hansen
▶ J. Xiong
Wijk aan Zee, 20.01.2017

38.♖xd5! exd5 [38...♖xd5 39.♖xd5
♕f7 40.♖xc5 bxc5 41.♘d6 ♘xd6
42.♗xd6 ♕xf2+ 43.♔h2+–] 39.♖xd5

♖df7 40.♖xc5 ♕e7 41.♖xf5 gxf4
42.♖xf4 1–0

(16)

▷ S. Sethuraman
► K. Sundararajan
Gibraltar Masters, 25.01.2017

16.♘xc5! dxc5 17.♕xc5+ ♔b8 [17...
♔d7 18.♗b5#] 18.♕e5+ ♔a8 19.♕xe6
fxe4 20.♗e2 ♖d2 21.♕c4±

(17)

▷ L. Dek
► E. Bacrot
Internet Pro League Rapid,
25.01.2017

26...♗xe3! 27.♘xe3 [27.♕xe3 ♖xg2
28.♖xg2 ♕xd1+–+] 27...♕xh2+!
28.♔xh2 ♖h6+ 29.♕h4 ♖xh4# 0–1

(18)

▷ J. Salomon
► M. Vachier Lagrave
Gibraltar Masters, 26.01.2017

25...♗xb3! 26.♕f3 [26.♖xb3 ♕xg2#]
26...♕xf3 27.♖xf3 ♗xa2 28.♖xf4
♘h5 29.♖g4 f5 0–1

(19)

▷ B. Gledura
► H. Nakamura
Gibraltar Masters, 27.01.2017

21...♘b6! 22.♘fd2 [22.♗xb6 ♗xc4!
23.♖xc4 ♖xa3 24.♕c2 ♖xd1+ 25.♕xd1
♕xc4–+] 22...♘xc4 23.♘xc4 ♘a5
0–1

(20)

▷ H. Nakamura
► E. Iturrizaga Bonelli
Gibraltar Masters, 28.01.2017

28.♕f3! 1–0[28.♕f3 ♗xe4 29.♕f8+
♖xf8 30.♖xf8#]

(21)

▷ S. Sethuraman
► I. Cheparinov
Gibraltar Masters, 29.01.2017

20...♘xg2! 21.♖g1 [21.♔xg2 ♘f4+
22.♔g1 ♕xh3–+] 21...♘2f4 22.♘f5
exd4 23.cxd4 ♕c6 24.♕xc6 bxc6
25.♖ge1 ♖ab8 –+

(22)

▷ S. Docx
► S. Sethuraman
Gibraltar Masters, 30.01.2017

23...♘e7! [23...♖xe2 24.♕f3 ♖xb2∓]
24.♕h5 [24.♗xe7 ♕xd5 25.♖c5
♖xe7–+] 24...♘xc6 25.♗c5 ♖e4
26.♖d1 ♖e5 27.dxe5 ♕xd1+ 28.♔h2
♕d5 0–1

(23)

▷ Z. Izoria
► J. Sheng
Internet Pro League Rapid,
01.02.2017

24...♖xf4+! 25.♔g1 [25.♔h3 ♕e6+
26.♔g2 ♖f2+ 27.♔g1 ♕c6 28.♕c1
♖g2+! 29.♔f1 ♖c2–+] 25...♖f2
26.♕c1 ♖g2+! 27.♔f1 ♖c2 0–1

(24)

▷ I. Cheparinov
► D. Fridman
Gibraltar Masters, 01.02.2017

73.e4! a4 [73...dxe4 74.♖xc6+ ♔xc6
75.♗xe4++–] 74.e5+ ♔d7 75.f6 a3
76.♗f5+ ♔c7 77.f7 a2 78.♖a1 +–

(25)

▷ B. Gledura
► V. Topalov
Gibraltar Masters, 02.02.2017

34...♕e1+! 0–1[34...♕e1+ 35.♗xe1
♖xe1#]

(26)

▷ E. Espinosa Veloz
► C. Gomes Garrido
Cuban Championship Villa Clara,
02.02.2017

27...♖d8!! [27...♕xe5? 28.♖b3 ♖xb3
29.♕xb3+ ♔c8 30.♕a4 f5 31.♕a6+=]
28.♖f1 [28.♖xd5 ♖b1+–+] 28...♗d3
0–1

(27)

▷ A. Donchenko
► A. Naiditsch
Gibraltar Masters, 02.02.2017

42...♘a1! 43.♖xd4 [43.♖a4 ♖d2!
44.♖xa1 ♖xd3+ 45.♔f2 ♖xb3–+] 43...
♘xb3 44.♖b4 ♘d2+ 45.♔e3 ♘f1+
46.♔f3 ♘h2+ 47.♔e3 ♖g2 48.♖b3
h5 49.♖a3 ♖xg3+ 50.♔f2 h4 51.♖c3
♘f3 0–1

(28)

▷ J. Lopez Martinez
► J. Guerra Mendez
Catalan League, 04.02.2017

26.♖d8+! ♔g7 27.gxf5! gxf5 [27...
♖xe4 28.f6+ ♔h6 29.♖h8#; 27...
♕b6+ 28.♔h2 gxf5 29.♕xc4+–]
28.♕e3 ♕c6 29.♖d6 ♖c1+ 30.♔h2
1–0

(29)

▷ N. Grandelius
► S. Ivanov
Swedish League, 04.02.2017

22.f4! 1–0[22.f4 ♕f6 23.♘xe4 dxe4
24.♕xd6+–]

(30)

▷ W. So
► M. Vachier Lagrave
Internet Pro League Rapid,
11.02.2017

28.♗c5! bxc5 29.b6 ♗h6 [29...♘d6
30.dxc5+-] **30.f4!** [30.♔f2 cxd4
31.b7 dxe3+ 32.♔g3 h4+ 33.♔g4 f5+
34.♔xh4 ♗f4-+] **30...c4 31.♗xg6+**
♔xg6 32.b7 f5 1-0

[31]

▷ **J. Quesada Perez**
▶ **L. Van Wely**
Internet Pro League Rapid,
11.02.2017

36.♖d7! ♖c4 [36...♘xd7 37.exd7+-]
37.e7! ♘xd7 38.♗xd7 ♖e4 1-0

[32]

▷ **M. Ragger**
▶ **J. Maiwald**
Bundesliga, 18.02.2017

13.♗c5! ♘ce7 [13... ♗xd6 14.♘xd6++-
] **14.♕d3** 1-0

[33]

▷ **S. Bromberger**
▶ **N. Grandelius**
Bundesliga, 19.02.2017

19.♖f4! f5 [19...♘xe3 20.♖h4 f5
21.g6+-; 19...♘6e5 20.♖h4 f6 21.♗d4
fxg5 (21...♕e8 22.♕h7+ ♔f7 23.gxf6
♔xf6 24.♖g4+-) 22.♕h8+ ♔f7
23.♖f1+ ♕f6 (23...♔e7 24.♕xg7++-)
24.♖xf6+ ♔xf6 25.♖h6+ ♔f7
26.♕h7+-] **20.g6 ♗f6 21.♕h7+**
♔f8 22.♕h8+ ♔e7 23.♖xg7+ ♔e8
24.♖h4 ♗f8 [24...♕e7 25.♖h8+
♔d7 26.♖h7! ♕xg7 27.♖xg7+ ♘e7

28.♗g5+-] **25.♖h8 ♖xh8 26.♕f7#**
1-0

[34]

▷ **S. Bogdanovish**
▶ **V. Onischuk**
Lutsk Nebesna Sotnya Memorial
Rapid, 19.02.2017

29.♖d1+! ♔c8 30.c6 ♗xc6 31.♗a6+
♗b7 32.♕a8+ ♕b8 33.♖d8+ 1-0

[35]

▷ **M. Bezold**
▶ **McShane,L**
Bundesliga, 19.02.2017

29...♘xh2! 30.♗xh2 [30.♔xh2
♕xf2+ 31.♔h1 ♕xg3-+] **30...♗xh2**
31.♖h1 [31.♔xh2 ♕xf2+ 32.♔h1
♕h4+ 33.♔g1 ♕g3+ 34.♔f1 ♖e5-+]
31...♗e5 32.♔f1 ♔g7∓

[36]

▷ **A. Motylev**
▶ **A. Donchenko**
Aeroflot Open Moscow, 21.02.2017

20.♗d8+! ♔xd8 21.♕b7 ♗a3
22.♕xa8 ♔c8 23.♗c6 1-0

[37]

▷ **A. Riazantsev**
▶ **D. Jakovenko**
Sharjah FIDE GP, 22.02.2017

19...♕h3! 20.f4 ♕g4+ 0-1

(38)

▷ V. Durarbayli
► K. Dragun
Internet Pro League Rapid,
22.02.2017

25...♕xd3! 26.♖xd3 ♖c1+ 0–1[26...
♖c1+ 27.♗xc1 ♖e1#]

(39)

▷ M. Cornette
► M. Nikolov
Rochefort Open, 22.02.2017

29...♕c6! 30.♖d3 [30.♗a5 ♕c5+–+;
30.♗f4 ♕b6+–+] 30...♕xc7 31.e5
♕c2 32.♖d7 ♕c5+ 0–1

(40)

▷ A. Kosteniuk
► A. Muzychuk
Fide World Cup Teheran, 23.02.2017

56...♞g5! 57.♖b3 [57.h4 ♖xe5!
58.♕xe5 (58.hxg5 ♖e1+ 59.♔h2 ♖h1#)
58...♞f3+–+] 57...♞xh3+ 58.♔h2
♞xf2! 59.♕xf2 ♖xe5 60.♕b2 ♕xa4
61.♖f3 ♕b5 62.♕c3 ♖e2+ 63.♔g1
♕b1+ 64.♖f1 ♕b6+ 0–1

(41)

▷ D. Harika
► Z. Tan
Fide World Cup Teheran, 25.02.2017

12.♕h4! ♖e8 [12...hxg5 13.♞xg5+–]
13.♗xh6 d5 14.e5 ♞d7 15.♞g5 ♗xh6
16.♕xh6 ♞f8 17.♖f4 1–0

(42)

▷ R. Buhmann
► N. Vitiugov
Aeroflot Open Moscow, 25.02.2017

29...♖e1+! 30.♔xe1 [30.♞xe1 ♕xf2#]
30...♗xf2+ 0–1

(43)

▷ R. Cvek
► V. Laznicka
Czech League, 26.02.2017

52...♗xd5! 0–1[52...♗xd5 53.♗xd5
♕c1+ 54.♕d1 (54.♔f2 ♕f1#) 54...
♕xe3+–+]

(44)

▷ M. Pavlovic
► S. Swapnil
Aeroflot Open Moscow, 27.02.2017

35...♞xd3! 36.♖b1 [36.♖xc7 ♞e1+–
+] 36...♞c5 37.♖e1 ♕d6 –+

(45)

▷ P. Maghsoodloo
► D. Paravyan
Aeroflot Open Moscow, 01.03.2017

33...♞xf4! 34.gxf4 ♖xf4 35.♖d2
[35.♖e2 ♖f3 36.♖g2 ♖xh3+ 37.♔g1
♕h5–+] 35...♖f1 36.♖g2 ♕f6
37.♖ee2 h5! 38.♖g3 h4 39.♖g4

♕c6 40.♖ge4 ♕d6+ 41.♖e5 ♖8f2+!
42.♖xf2 ♕xe5+ 43.♔g2 ♖e1 –+

(46)

▷ K. Lie
▶ O. Saevareid
Norwegian League, 03.03.2017

21.♘xe6! fxe6 22.♕xe6+ ♔f8
1–0[22...♔f8 23.♗h7+–; 22...♔h8
23.♕g6 ♔g8 24.♕h7+ ♔f8 25.♗g6+–]

(47)

▷ I. Nikolaidis
▶ A. Karagiannis
Greek Championship Thessaloniki,
04.03.2017

25.♗xe4! R8xe4 26.♖xe4 ♖xe4
27.♘c5 ♖e7 28.d6! ♘xd6 29.♖d1 1–0

(48)

▷ T. Hillarp Persson
▶ D. Fendrich
Swedish League, 04.03.2017

24.♕xh7+! ♔xh7 25.♖h3# 1–0

(49)

▷ S. Lorparizangeneh
▶ P. Darini
Iranian Championship Teheran,
05.03.2017

48...♖d1+! 49.♔e2 [49.♔f2 ♗e1+
50.♔e2 ♗f3+ 51.♔f1 ♖xg3#] 49...
♗f3+ 0–1

(50)

▷ R. Jumabayev
▶ A. Shabalov
Jurmala Tal Memorial Rapid,
05.03.2017

24.♘xf7! ♘d5 [24...♖xd1 25.♘xh6+
♔g7 26.♖xd1+–] 25.♘xh6+ ♔g7
26.♗g5 ♘b6 27.♘g4 +–

(51)

▷ S. Ganguly
▶ S. Lu
India-China Liaocheng, 07.03.2017

41...e2! 42.♖g1 ♖d1! 43.♘f3+ ♖xg1+
44.♔xg1 ♕b1+ [44...♘h3+ 45.♔h1
e1♕+ 46.♘xe1 ♕f1#] 45.♔f2 ♕f1+
46.♔e3 e1♕+ 47.♘xe1 ♕xe1+
48.♔f3 [48.♔xf4 ♕d2+–+] 48...
♕e2+ 0–1

(52)

▷ M. Bagheri
▶ P. Maghsoodloo
Iranian Championship, 07.03.2017

14...♘d3+! 15.♕xd3 [15.♔f1 ♗xd4
16.♗xd3 ♗xc3 17.♕xc3 ♘xd5–+] 15...
♗xd3 16.♖xd3 ♗xd4 17.♖xd4 ♕g5
0–1

(53)

▷ G. Jones
► C. Henriquez Villagra
Internet Pro League Rapid,
08.03.2017

19.Nxe6! 1–0 [19.Nxe6 Qxe3 20.Nxf8++-]

(54)

▷ E. Agrest
► N. Pert
Internet Rapid, 08.03.2017

49.Nf8+! Kh6 [49...Kh8 50.Ne6++-] **50.Ne6 Bxe6 51.Qh8+** 1–0 [51.Qh8+ Kg6 52.Rxe6+ Kf7 53.Qe8#]

(55)

▷ S. Lorparizangeneh
► S. Mousavi
Iranian Championship Teheran,
12.03.2017

22...Qh5! [22...Rf2 23.Qd3 Bg4-+] **23.h3** [23.Qxh5 Rf1#] **23...Bxh3** 0–1

(56)

▷ M. Gagunashvili
► A. Gharagyozyan
Baghdad Open, 17.03.2017

14.Nc4! Qc7 [14...dxc4 15.Bxh7+ Kxh7 16.Rxd6+-] **15.Ncxe5 Re8 16.Rfe1 Nc5** [16...f6 17.Bxh7+ Kxh7 18.Qd3+ Kg8 19.Qxd5+ Kh7 20.Qf7+-] **17.Ng5 Nxd3 18.Qxd3**

Nxe5 19.Qxh7+ Kf8 20.Qh8+ Ke7 21.Qxg7 1–0

(57)

▷ J. Glud
► M. Matthiesen
Danish League, 19.03.2017

21.Rxc7! Qxc7 22.Nf6+ 1–0

(58)

▷ G. Antal
► R. Farkas
Budapest Spring Open, 20.03.2017

27...Qxf2+! 0–1[27...Qxf2+ 28.Rxf2 Rb1+-+]

(59)

▷ H. Odeev
► A. Timofeev
Budapest Spring Open, 21.03.2017

20.Bxb7! Qxb7 21.Rxd6! 1–0[21.Rxd6 Bxd6 (21...0-0 22.Rxd7 Bxh2+ 23.Kxh2 Rxd7 24.Re1+-) 22.Rxe6+ Kf8 23.Qxd6++-]

(60)

▷ K. Stupak
► H. Odeev
Budapest Spring Open, 22.03.2017

20.Qxh6+! Bxh6 21.Rxh6+ Kg7 22.Rh7+ Kf6 23.Ne4+ Kg6 24.Rxe7 Nd3+ 25.Kd2 Nxc1 26.Kxc1 c6 27.Bb3 Bf5 28.Nd6 1–0

(61)

▷ D. Sadzikowski
► A. Mista
Polish Championship Warsaw,
22.03.2017

44.♕d8! [44.♖c8? ♕xf6=] 44...♕e3
[44...♕d6 45.♕xd6 ♗xd6 46.♖c6+-]
45.♕xf8+! ♔xf8 46.♖c8# 1-0

(62)

▷ G. Papp
► L. Kessler
Austrian League, 23.03.2017

18.♘h5! ♖c8 [18...gxh5 19.♕g3++-]
19.♘g7 ♗f6 [19...♗f8 20.♘xe6 fxe6
21.♗xf8+-] 20.♘xe8 ♗xd4 21.♖xe6
♕h4 22.♘d6 fxe6 23.♕f7+ ♔h8
24.♘xc8 ♕xh6 25.♘e7 ♕c1+
26.♔h2 ♗e5+ 27.g3 ♗xg3+ 28.♔g2
1-0

(63)

▷ H. Wang
► S. Sethuraman
Sharjah Masters, 25.03.2017

23.♖g3! ♖g8 [23...♕e7 24.♘e5+-]
24.♘d6 1-0[24.♘d6 ♖xg4 25.♘f7+
♔g8 26.♖xg4+ ♔f8 27.♘xd8+-;
24.♕xg8+ ♕xg8 25.♖xg8+ ♔xg8
26.♘b6+ ♔f8 27.♘xa8+-]

(64)

▷ A. Tari
► A. Goganov
Swedish League, 25.03.2017

23...♖h8! 24.♕g5 [24.♕xh8 ♕e3-+]
24...♖h5! 0-1[24...♖h5 25.♕xh5 ♕e3
26.♕e2 ♗g4-+]

(65)

▷ A. Kveinys
► L. Stauskas
Baltic zt Vilnius, 25.03.2017

19.♖xc8! ♖xc8 20.♖xd5 ♖c2 [20...
exd5 21.♕xc8++-] 21.♖h5 ♖xb2
22.♖xh7 g6 23.♖h8+ ♔g7 1-0

(66)

▷ K. Alekseenko
► E. Levin
St. Petersburg, 25.03.2017

17...♗xa3! 18.♘d4 [18.bxa3 ♕xa3+
19.♔b1 ♕b4+! 20.♔a1 ♘xe5 21.♘a2
♘xd3 22.♘xb4 ♘xb4-+] 18...♘xe5
19.♕h3 ♔b8! 20.♘xe6 [20.bxa3
♕xa3+ 21.♔b1 ♘c4-+] 20...♘c4
21.♖xd8+ ♖xd8 22.♘xd8 ♗xb2+ -+

(67)

▷ E. Agrest
► H. Tikkanen
Swedish League, 25.03.2017

40.♗xe5! ♗xe5 41.♘d3+- 1-0

(68)

▷ V. Kovalev
▶ D. Popovic
Budapest Spring Open, 26.03.2017

33.♗c5! 1–0[33.♗c5 ♔f8 (*33...♖xc5 34.♕e8#*) 34.♕xc8#]

(69)

▷ M. Manolache
▶ V. Nevednichy
Romanian Championsip, 28.03.2017

25.♖xb5! 1–0[25.♖xb5 axb5 (*25... ♕xb4 26.♖xb4 ♔c7 27.♖ab3+-*) 26.♕xe7+-]

(70)

▷ A. Kaliksteyn
▶ T. Ringoir
Charlotte GM, 29.03.2017

28...♘xc3! 0–1[28...♘xc3 29.♕xc3 (*29.♕xa4 ♖xa4 30.♖a1 ♘e2+ 31.♔f1 c3–+*) 29...♕xd1+–+]

(71)

▷ M. Bluebaum
▶ P. Vishnu
Sharjah Masters, 29.03.2017

17.♕b2! 1–0[17.♕b2 a6 18.♘b3 ♕xa3 19.♕xa3 axb5 20.♕c1 bxc4 21.♕xc4±]

(72)

▷ B. Adhiban
▶ H. Wang
Sharjah Masters, 29.03.2017

28...♘xc5! 29.♕c2 [29.dxc5 ♕xf5–+; 29.♕xd7 ♘cxd7–+] **29...♘a6 30.♕b3 ♗d6 31.♖gf1 ♘xb4** –+

(73)

▷ A. Adly
▶ D. Anton Guijarro
Sharjah Masters, 31.03.2017

47.♖f7+! 1–0[47.♖f7+ ♔g8 (*47...♔e8 48.♘d6+ ♔d8 49.♖d7#*) 48.♘f6+ ♔h8 49.♖f8+ ♔g7 50.♖g8#]

(74)

▷ L. Pantsulaia
▶ V. Raahul
Dubai Open, 04.04.2017

17.♖xa6! ♗xa6 18.♘c6 ♕d7 19.♘xe7+ ♔h8 20.♘xd5 +-

(75)

▷ F. Caruana
▶ G. Kamsky
American Championship, 04.04.2017

17.♘xa6! 0–0 [17...♖xa6 18.♗xb5++-]
18.♘b4 f5 19.0–0 fxe4 20.♗xe4 +-

(76)

▷ V. Akobian
▶ F. Caruana
American Championship, 07.04.2017

77.♕a7+! ♔h6 [77...♔h8 78.♘f7+ ♔g7 (*78...♔g8 79.♘h6++-*) 79.♘d6++-] **78.♘g4+ ♔g5 79.♕xh7** 1–0

(77)

▷ Y. Zherebukh
► H. Nakamura
American Championship, 08.04.2017

18...♖xh2! 19.♖fd1 [19.♔xh2 ♘g4+−+; 19.♕xa7 ♖dh8−+] 19...♖dh8 20.♕xa7 e3! 21.♕xe3 ♘g4 0−1 [21...♘g4 22.♕f3 ♖h1+ 23.♘xh1 ♖xh1+ 24.♔xh1 ♕h2#]

(78)

▷ P. Stuemer
► G. Papp
Karlsruhe Grenke Open, 13.04.2017

29...♕xf2+! 0−1[29...♕xf2+ 30.♕xf2 ♖xe1#]

(79)

▷ J. Guerra Mendez
► V. Baklan
La Roda Open, 15.04.2017

48.♘xg6! hxg6 [48...♘xg5 49.♖f8#] 49.♕xg6+ ♔h8 50.♕e8+ ♔h7 51.♖f6 ♕xd4 [51...♕d6 52.♖xe6 ♕h2+ 53.♔g5 ♕d2+ 54.♖e3+−] 52.♕xe6 ♕e4 53.♕xe4+ dxe4 54.♖e6 +−

(80)

▷ A. Demuth
► D. Nasshan
Karlsruhe Grenke Open, 15.04.2017

19.♘xd5! ♖xc2 [19...♘xd5 20.♘c6+−] 20.♘xe7+ ♔h8 21.♘xc2 +−

(81)

▷ J. Blit
► D. Flores
Mar del Plata Open, 15.04.2017

20.f4! ♖f5 [20...exf3 21.♖xe5 dxe5 22.♕xh7+ ♔f8 23.♖f1 ♗d5 24.♗g6+−; 20...g5 21.♕g3 ♖f5 22.♖xe4+−] 21.♗xe4 ♖f6 22.♕xh7+ ♔f8 23.♗g6 +−

(82)

▷ S. Martinovic
► L. Lodici
Karlsruhe Grenke Open, 16.04.2017

20.♖xc6! ♕xc6 21.♘f6+ 1−0

(83)

▷ V. Kramnik
► P. Svidler
Chess Challenge Blitz, 17.04.2017

38.♕f7! 1−0[38.♕f7 gxf4 (38...♕e2+ 39.♔h3 ♕f1+ 40.♔g4+−) 39.♕xf6+ ♔h7 40.♘g5+ ♔g8 41.♕f7+ ♔h8 42.♕h7#]

(84)

▷ V. Anand
► B. Gelfand
Chess Challenge Blitz, 17.04.2017

51.♕a4! f5 [51...♗c5 52.♕a8+−] 52.♖e8+ ♔f6 53.♕h4+ ♔g7 54.♕h8+ 1−0

(85)

▷ D. Flores
▶ A. Bachmann
Szmetan Memorial Buenos Aires,
20.04.2017

19.♘xd5! 1–0[19.♘xd5 exd5 (*19...*
♕d8 20.♘xe7 ♕xe7 21.♗xa8 ♖xa8
22.b4+–) 20.e6++–]

(86)

▷ E. Blomqvist
▶ A. Savage
Reykjavik Open, 22.04.2017

22.♕f6! 1–0[22.♕f6 exf6 23.♖xe8#]

(87)

▷ Z. Almasi
▶ A. Ramirez
Reykjavik open, 22.04.2017

43.♘f5+! ♗xf5 [43...gxf5 44.♕xe5+–]
44.♕xe5 fxg3 45.hxg3 ♗g4 46.♕f4+
♔g7 47.♖xc6 ♖xd3 48.♖c7+ ♖d7
49.♗f3! +–

(88)

▷ H. Fuchs
▶ A. Graf
Bundesliga 2, 23.04.2017

28...♘b3! 0–1[28...♘b3 29.axb3 (*29.*
♕e1 ♘xc1 30.♗xc1 ♗xf1 31.♖xf1–+)
29...axb3 30.♖xc8 ♕a2+ 31.♔c1 ♕a1#]

(89)

▷ J. Bai
▶ C. Wang
Chinese Championship, 23.04.2017

40...♖xf1+! 41.♕xf1 ♕e3+ 0–1[41...
♕e3+ 42.♔g2 c1♕ –+]

(90)

▷ B. Jobava
▶ K. Landa
Reykjavik Open, 24.04.2017

43.♖xa7! ♔xd6 44.♖d7+! ♔xd7
45.a7 ♖xc2 46.a8♕ +–

(91)

▷ A. Saric
▶ Z. Kozul
Croatian Championship Valpovo,
26.04.2017

86...♕e6+! 87.♕xe6 fxe6 88.♔f6 g4
0–1

(92)

▷ M. Palac
▶ I. Saric
Croatian Championship Valpovo,
26.04.2017

41...f2+! 42.♘f3 ♕e2 0–1[42...♕e2
43.♕d6+ (*43.♖bb1 ♘b5–+*) 43...
♔e8 44.♕xc6+ ♔f8 45.♕f6+ ♔g8
46.♖bb1 ♖f8–+]

(93)

▷ A. Huzman
▶ N. Short
World Championship Seniors 50,
30.04.2017

43...♗xd4! 0–1[43...♗xd4 44.exd4 ♘c3#]

(94)

▷ C. Bauer
▶ R. Stern
Bundesliga, 30.04.2017

23.♘xf7! ♖xf7 [23...♔xf7 24.♗xe6+ ♔g6 (24...♔e8 25.♕a4+ ♘b5 26.d5+-) 25.♕d3+ ♔h6 26.♗xd6 ♗xd6 27.♕h3+ ♔g6 28.♗b3+-; 23...♘xf7 24.♗xb8 ♕xb8 25.♗xe6 ♗d6 26.♖b1+-] 24.♗xe6 ♔f8 25.♗xf7 ♘xf7 26.♖xe7 +-

(95)

▷ S. Bromberger
▶ J. Granda Zuniga
Bundesliga, 01.05.2017

33.♘g5! ♕c1+ [33...♖xe3 34.♖a8++-] 34.♕xc1 ♘xc1 35.♘xf7+ ♔g8 36.♘e5 [36.♖xb1+-] 36...♘e2+ 37.♔f2 ♘xf4 38.♖xb1 ♖xe5 39.♗xe5 ♘d3+ 40.♔e3 ♘xe5 41.♔d4 ♘d7 42.♖c1 c5+ 43.♔d5 1–0

(96)

▷ S. Saydaliev
▶ K. Stupak
Agzamov Memorial Tashkent,
04.05.2017

22...h5! 23.♕f3 e4 0–1

(97)

▷ J. Stocek
▶ R. Biolek
Czech Championship Ostrava,
06.05.2017

29.♘d4! 1–0[29.♘d4 ♖xd4 (29...♖e8 30.♘e6+ ♖xe6 31.♕xe6+-) 30.♕xd4 cxd4 31.♖xc7+-]

(98)

▷ V. Babula
▶ P. Haba
Czech Championship, 06.05.2017

28.♕e7! 1–0[28.♕e7 ♖xg3 (28...♕f5 29.♕g7+ ♖xg7 30.♖e8+ ♖g8 31.♖gxg8#) 29.♕xf6+ ♖g7 30.♖e8+ ♕g8 31.♖xg8+ ♔xg8 32.♕xb2+-]

(99)

▷ H. Asis Gargatagli
▶ M. Narciso Dublan
Catalan League, 06.05.2017

23.♖xd4! exd4 24.♕e5+ 1–0[24. ♕e5+ ♔g8 25.♗c4 ♗e6 26.♗xe6+-]

(100)

▷ L. Fressinet
▶ E. Bacrot
Balagna Rapid Open, 07.05.2017

47...e1♖+! [47...e1♕+!–+] 48.♗xe1 ♗d4+ 49.♗f2 ♖e1# 0–1

(101)

▷ A. Shomoev
► G. Kamsky
Russian League Sochi, 08.05.2017

25.♞f6+! gxf6 26.♛g4+ ♞g6
27.♜xd8 ♜bxd8 +-

(102)

▷ Y. Roshka
► S. Bogdanovich
Lvov Rapid Cup, 08.05.2017

27...♝h3!! 0-1[27...♝h3 28.♝xh3
♜c1+ 29.♝f1 ♜xf1#]

(103)

▷ M. Oleksienko
► V. Bernadskiy
Lvov Rapid Cup, 08.05.2017

30...♜h1+! 31.♝xh1 ♞h3+ 0-1

(104)

▷ A. Giri
► E. Romanov
Russian League Sochi, 08.05.2017

30.♞xd4! ♜xd4 31.♝d3! 1-0[31.
♝b7+-; 31.♝d3 ♝xd3 (31...♜xe1+
32.♜xe1 ♜xd3 33.♜e8#) 32.♜xe8#]

(105)

▷ R. Mamedov
► V. Onischuk
Lvov Rapid Cup, 09.05.2017

15...c5! -+

(106)

▷ M. Kazhgaleyev
► A. Urazayev
Agzamov Memorial Tashkent,
09.05.2017

19.♞g4! ♞xe4 20.♝xd8 ♝xe1
21.♝xa5 ♝xa5 22.♛xe4 ♜ac8 23.♜c1
1-0

(107)

▷ S. Bogdanovich
► D. Kovalev
Lvov Rapid Cup, 09.05.2017

16.♝xh7+! ♚xh7 17.hxg4+ ♚g8 [17...
♚g6 18.♞h4+ ♚h7 19.♞f5+ ♚g8
20.♞e7#] 18.♝xe3 1-0

(108)

▷ A. Jankovic
► D. Raguz
Croatian Cup Mali Losinj, 11.05.2017

25.f3? [25.♝h5+!! ♚xh5 26.♛f7+ ♚g4
(26...♝g6 27.g4+ ♚xg4 28.♛xg6+-)
27.f3+ ♝xf3 28.gxf3+ ♚xf3 29.♛h5+
♚e4 30.♛g4+ ♚d3 31.♛f5++-] 25...
♜b7? [25...♜e8 26.♛d6 ♜bd8 27.♛a3
♝f5±] 26.♛e6 ♝f5 27.♝d3 1-0[27.
♝d3 ♝xd3 28.♛xc8+-]

(109)

▷ A. Brkic
► N. Sedlak
Croatian Cup Mali Losinj, 11.05.2017

55...♘xf4! 56.gxf4 ♖xf4+ 57.♔g5
[57.♔xh5 ♖h3+ 58.♔g5 ♖hh4–+]
57...♖g4+ 58.♔xh5 ♖g1 0–1[58...♖g1
59.♔h4 g5+ 60.♔h5 ♖h3#]

[110]

▷ F. Urkedal
► D. Akdag
Copenhagen Challenge Ballerup,
13.05.2017

26.♕xf5! 1–0[26.♕xf5 ♖xf5 27.♖h6#]

[111]

▷ P. Harikrishna
► P. Svidler
Fide GP Moscow, 14.05.2017

19...♗xc3+! 20.♕xc3 [20.♘xc3
♕xg5–+] 20...♕xe4+ 21.♗e3 [21.♕e3
♕xe3+ 22.fxe3–+] 21...e5 22.♕xc5
♘d4 –+

[112]

▷ A. Goganov
► J. Ibanez Aullana
Llucmajor Open, 14.05.2017

23.♕xf6+! 1–0[23.♘xc6 bxc6
24.♕xc6 ♕xc6 25.♖xc6±; 23.♕xf6+
♔xf6 24.♘d5+ ♔f7 25.♘xc7+–]

[113]

▷ A. Sokolov
► J. Moucheroud
French League, 19.05.2017

26.♗a5! ♖e8 27.♗h3 1–0

[114]

▷ M. Kanarek
► D. Mastrovasilis
Katowice Rapid, 20.05.2017

64...♔f6?? [64...h5!! 65.♔h8 (65.
gxh5 ♔f6=; 65.g5?? h4–+) 65...hxg4
66.hxg4 ♔g6 67.g5=] 65.h4 h5 66.g5+
♔f7 67.♔h8 1–0[67.g6+? ♔f6–+;
67.♔h8 g6 (67...♔f8 68.g6+–; 67...♔g6
68.♔g8+–) 68.♔h7+–]

[115]

▷ X. Bu
► R. Jumabayev
Asian Continental Open Chengdu,
20.05.2017

41.♗b5! ♕xb5 [41...♕c8 42.♗xd7
♘xd7 43.♖xd7+–] 42.♕xc3 1–0

[116]

▷ T. Bueder
► K. Tarlev
Bodensee Open Bregenz, 21.05.2017

29.♖xd3! ♕e4 [29...♖xd3 30.♕g5#]
30.♕c3+ 1–0

(117)

▷ S. Karjakin
► G. Meier
Internet Blitz, 24.05.2017

36.♘f5! exf5 37.♕e8+ ♔h7 38.♖xd6 ♖xd6 39.♖xd6 +-

(118)

▷ S. Lu
► J. Bai
Chinese League, 25.05.2017

31.♖xe6! fxe6 32.♖xe6 ♖b5 33.♕xc4 ♖b4 34.♕c7! ♖b1+ [34...♖f7 35.♕d6+-] 35.♔g2 ♖c1 36.♕xb7 ♖b1 37.♕d7 ♖f7 38.♕d5 ♖b5 39.♖e8# 1–0

(119)

▷ N. Bueter
► V. Epishin
Stuttgart Open, 26.05.2017

18...♕xe4! 0–1[18...♕xe4 19.♕xe4 ♘g3+ 20.♔h2 ♘xe4–+]

(120)

▷ P. Ponkratov
► I. Babikov
European Championship Minsk, 30.05.2017

17.♘xd5! exd5 18.♗xd5+ ♔h8 19.♗xc6 ♕f8 20.♗f3 +-

(121)

▷ S. Zhigalko
► A. Aleksandrov
European Championship Minsk, 02.06.2017

39.♕h8+! ♔xh8 40.♘xf7+ ♔g7 41.♘xd6±

(122)

▷ D. Mastrovasilis
► A. Volokitin
European Championship Minsk, 02.06.2017

19.♕c6+! ♖d7 [19...♔f8 20.♗xg5 ♗xb3 21.♕c7+-] 20.♖xe6+ fxe6 21.♕xe6+ ♔d8 [21...♗e7 22.♖b8+ ♖d8 23.♖xd8+ ♔xd8 24.♕xa2+-] 22.♖b8+ 1–0

(123)

▷ T. Harutyunian
► S. Movsesian
European Championship Minsk, 02.06.2017

45.♕d4+! ♔h7 46.♘d5 ♗c5 47.♘xe7 ♗xd4+ 48.♖xd4 ♖c1+ 49.♔f2 ♖c2+ 50.♔f3 +-

(124)

▷ D. Anton Guijarro
► O. Bortnyk
European Championship Minsk, 03.06.2017

20.e6! ♖c8 [20...♕c5+ 21.♕xc5
♘xc5 22.♘g6+ fxg6 23.♖xf8+ ♔xh7
24.e7+-; 20...♘f6 21.exf7+-] **21.♕f5
♘f6 22.exf7 ♕xf7 23.♗xf6 gxf6**
[23...♕xf6 24.♘g6+ ♔xh7 25.♘f8+
♔g8 26.♕h7+ ♔xf8 27.♖xf6+ gxf6
28.♖e1+-] **24.♘g6+ ♔g7 25.♘e5
♕e8 26.♖ae1 ♘c6 27.♕xf6+ ♔xh7
28.♘xc6 ♖xc6 29.♖e7+** 1–0

(125)

▷ **N. Heinichen**
▶ **A. Fier**
Maastricht Limburg Open,
04.06.2017

**27...♗xe5! 28.dxe5 b5 29.♖xc6 ♕xc6
30.♕b4 ♕c5** 0–1

(126)

▷ **M. Jurcik**
▶ **S. Maze**
European Championship Minsk,
06.06.2017

38...♖f1+! 39.♗xf1 ♖xa1+ 40.♔f2
[40.♔d2 ♗xf1 41.b6 ♖a8–+] **40...
♖xf1+ 41.♔e2 ♗e6** 0–1

(127)

▷ **T. Gelashvili**
▶ **F. Berkes**
European Championship Minsk,
06.06.2017

25.c6! ♕c8 [25...♕xc6 26.♗xf5+-]
26.♘xd5 ♗d8 [26...♘xe3 27.♘xf6+

gxf6 28.♖xe3+-] **27.♗f4 ♘e7
28.♕d3+-**

(128)

▷ **B. Jobava**
▶ **D. Mastrovasilis**
European Championship Minsk,
07.06.2017

50.♕g4+! [50.f7? ♕b3+ 51.♔h4
♕c4+ 52.♔h5 ♕e2+ 53.♔h6 ♕h2+
54.♔g7 ♕xe5+ 55.♔f8 ♕b8+ 56.♔e7
♕c7+=] **50...♔xe5 51.f7** 1–0 [51.f7
♕a3+ 52.♕g3++-]

(129)

▷ **G. Jones**
▶ **B. Jobava**
European Championship Minsk,
08.06.2017

**23...♖xf2! 24.♕xf2 ♖xf2 25.♔xf2
♕f6+** 0–1 [25...♕f6+ 26.♔g1 ♕b2–+]

(130)

▷ **C. Ali Marandi**
▶ **S. Bogdanovich**
European Championship Minsk,
08.06.2017

30.♘f6!! 1–0 [30.♘f6 ♖xf6 (30...♗a6
31.♖xh7#) 31.♖xe8+]

(131)

▷ **F. Berkes**
► **J. Tomczak**
European Championship Minsk,
10.06.2017

63...Rb3?? [63...Kd5! 64.b6+ Kc4 65.b7 (65.Ra4+ Kb3 66.b7 Rc7=) 65...Rb3 66.b8Q Rxb8 67.Kxb8 Rb3=] **64.b6 Kd6 65.b7 Kc7 66.Rc5+ Kd6 67.Rc1 Kd5 68.b8Q** 1-0

(132)

▷ **Y. Yu**
► **X. Xu**
Chinese League, 12.06.2017

14.Ng5! 1-0 [14.Ng5 Bxg2 15.Bxf6+-]

(133)

▷ **C. Cruz**
► **H. Panesso Rivera**
American Continental Medellin,
14.06.2017

30.Bxd6! 1-0[30.Bxd6 Rxd6 (30...Ke6 31.Nxe5 Rxd6 32.Nxc6+-; 30...Nxd6 31.Nxe5++-) 31.Nxe5+ Kf6 32.Rxd6+ Rxd6 33.Rxd6+ Nxd6 34.Nxc6+-]

(134)

▷ **S. Sevian**
► **R. Vasquez Schroder**
American Continental Medellin,
15.06.2017

23.Qg6! Qxe5 24.Rhf1! Rff7 [24...Rf6 25.Qe8+ Rf8 26.Qxf8#] **25.Qh7+ Kf8 26.Qh8+ Ke7 27.Rxf7+** 1-0[27.Rxf7+ Kxf7 28.Rf1+ Ke7 29.Qf8+ Kd7 30.Rf7#]

(135)

▷ **C. Gokerkan**
► **V. Malakhatko**
Cesme Open, 15.06.2017

23.Rxe4! fxe4 24.Qxe4 g6 25.Ne7+ Kg7 26.Qe5+ Rf6 27.Qxb8 Qxe7 28.Qxc8 1-0

(136)

▷ **R. Li**
► **A. He**
Las Vegas National Open, 17.06.2017

19.Rxf6! Rxf6 20.Rxf6 Qc6 21.Bd5 Qb6 22.Qxg6 hxg6 23.Rf3 Bxh2+ 24.Kh1 Bf4 25.Rh3+ 1-0

(137)

▷ **V. Rasulov**
► **D. Magalashvili**
Cesme Open, 18.06.2017

17.Qxd5! cxd5 18.Nf6+ Kd8 19.Ng4+ Kd7 20.Nxh2 dxe5 21.Bf6 Bd6 22.Ng4 1-0

(138)

▷ **A. Fier**
► **A. Ramirez**
American Continental Medellin
Rapid, 18.06.2017

34.♕b5! ♕xe4+ 35.♔a2 ♔d7 [35...
♕c2 36.♖xd6 0–0 37.♕xc6+-]
36.♕b7+ ♔e6 [36...♖c7 37.♖xd6+
♔xd6 38.♕xe4+-] 37.♕xf7# 1–0

(139)

▷ K. Sasikiran
► R. Robson
World Team Championship,
20.06.2017

27.♖e1!! [27.♕xd7 ♘f6 28.♕xc6
♖d8+ 29.♔e1 (29.♔c2 ♕xf5+ 30.♔b3
♖c8!∓) 29...♖e8+ 30.♘e2 ♕xf5
31.♖d1±] 27...♖g8 [27...♖d8 28.♕e7
♖g8 29.♕xd7+-; 27...♘f6 28.♖xe8+
♗xe8 29.♕f8+ ♘g8 30.♕xe8 ♕xf5
31.♕xc6 b4 32.axb4 axb4 33.♘e4+-]
28.♕xd7 ♘xf2 [28...♘f6 29.♕xc6
♕xf5 30.♕xb5 ♖d8+ 31.♔c1+-;
28...♕g2 29.♗e8 ♕xf2+ 30.♘e2+-]
29.♖e8 +-

(140)

▷ K. Lagno
► L. Javakhishvili
World Team Championship,
20.06.2017

26.♕d4! ♕d8 27.♘h5+ ♔f8 28.♕c5+
♔e8 [28...♔g8 29.♕xc1+-] 29.♘g7+
1–0 [29.♘g7+ ♔d7 30.♘e5#]

(141)

▷ O. Ladva
► A. Neiksans
Baltic zt Liepaja, 20.06.2017

34.♖xg7+! ♕xg7 [34...♔xg7
35.♗d4+-] 35.♗d4 f5 [35...f6
36.♘e4+-] 36.♕h4 ♖e5 [36...g5
37.♕h5 ♕xd4 38.♕h7+ ♔f8 39.♕xf5+
♔g8 40.♖h7+-] 37.♗xe5 dxe5 38.d6
g5 39.♕h5 ♖d8 40.♘d5 +-

(142)

▷ S. Mamedyarov
► M. Carlsen
Paris GCT Rapid, 21.06.2017

28...♗f3! 29.a5 [29.♘xf3 ♕xf3
30.♕c1 ♖e2 31.♕f1 ♕e4-+] 29...♖e2
30.♕d1 ♗g4 31.f3 ♕e6 0–1

(143)

▷ I. Nepomniachtchi
► J. Duda
World Team Championship Khan-
ty-Mansiysk, 23.06.2017

32.♖xf6! ♖d1+ [32...exf6 33.♘f5+-]
33.♔h2! [33.♘xd1 exf6 34.♕xf6
♕xc2+-] 33...♕a1 34.♕xg5+ ♔f8
35.♖h6 ♖h1+ 36.♔g3 ♕e1+ 37.♔f3+-

(144)

▷ A. Donchenko
► R. Frischmann
German Championship Apolda,
23.06.2017

23.♖xh7+! [23.♕e4+-] 23...♔xh7
24.♕h1+ ♔g7 25.♕h6# 1–0

(145)

▷ W. So
▶ M. Carlsen
Paris GCT Blitz, 24.06.2017

43...♕a1+! 44.♔h2 ♘e5 45.♕f5
♘xd7 46.♕xd7 ♖e8 47.♘d5 ♕e5+
48.♗g3 ♕xh5+ 0–1

(146)

▷ G. Popilski
▶ Y. Zherebukh
New York International Open,
24.06.2017

21...f5! 0–1 [21...f5 22.gxf6 (22.♕xf5
♗xg2+ 23.♔xg2 ♖xe2+–+) 22...♘xf6
23.♕g3 ♖xe2–+]

(147)

▷ S. Mamedyarov
▶ V. Topalov
Paris GCT Blitz, 25.06.2017

20.♗xf6! ♗xf6 21.♖xg4 ♕xg4
22.♕xc6+ 1–0

(148)

▷ B. Rogulj
▶ B. Kurajica
Karlovac, 27.06.2017

19.♗c5! ♕e6 20.♕f3 1–0

(149)

▷ M. Carlsen
▶ L. Aronian
Leuven GCT Blitz, 28.06.2017

29.♖xf6! gxf6 [29...♕xf3 30.♖xf3+-]
30.♗xd5 ♕xf3 31.♗xf3 ♖fe8 32.♖c2
♖c8 33.♖xc8 ♖xc8 34.♗xf6 +-

(150)

▷ S. Poormosavi
▶ P. Darini
Asia zt Teheran, 30.06.2017

22.♖hd1!! ♕f5 [22...bxc3 23.♖xe6+!
fxe6 24.♕d7#] 23.♕d4! bxc3
24.♖d8+ ♔e7 25.♖d7+ 1–0 [25.
♖d7+ ♔e8 26.♕b4 ♕xf4+ 27.♔b1
♕f6 28.♖e7+ ♕xe7 29.♕a4+ ♕d7
30.♕xd7#]

(151)

▷ E. Moradiabadi
▶ D. Aaron
Philadelphia World Open, 01.07.2017

17.♕b5! b6 18.♕a6+ ♔b8 19.cxb6
cxb6 [19...axb6 20.♖xb6+ cxb6
21.♗f4++-] 20.♖xb6+ ♔a8 21.♖xc6
gxh3 22.♗f1 ♖e8 23.♗f4 1–0

(152)

▷ M. Carlsen
▶ V. Ivanchuk
Leuven GCT Blitz, 01.07.2017

22.♕a2! 1–0

(153)

▷ M. Krasenkow
► E. Safarli
Porticcio Open, 02.07.2017

61.♖f2+! ♔g5 62.h7 ♘d4 63.♖h2
1–0

(154)

▷ L. Aronian
► M. Vachier Lagrave
Leuven GCT Blitz, 02.07.2017

43...♖c2+! 0–1 [43...♖c2+ 44.♔xc2
♔xe3 45.b5 ♔f2 46.♗d3 ♔xg2 47.b6
♔xf3 48.♗a6 ♗c8–+]

(155)

▷ L. Aronian
► I. Nepomniachtchi
Leuven GCT Blitz, 02.07.2017

**27.g4! ♕xh4 28.♕xe5+ ♔g8
29.♕xb8 ♕xf2 30.♕xb5 +-**

(156)

▷ I. Rozum
► D. Khismatullin
Russian Higher League Sochi,
03.07.2017

24.♖xc7+! ♖xc7 25.♗xe6+ 1–0
[25.♗xe6+ ♔d6 26.♖xc7 ♔xc7
27.♗xd5+-]

(157)

▷ V. Zvjaginsev
► M. Antipov
Russian Higher League Sochi,
04.07.2017

**18.♘d5! ♕xd5 19.♕xd5+ ♘xd5
20.♖xe8+ ♔f7 21.♖ae1 b5** [21...♘xf4
22.♖1e7#] **22.♗d6 ♗b7 23.♖8e7+**
1–0

(158)

▷ P. Czarnota
► A. Istratescu
Greek League, 04.07.2017

25.♕xf7! ♖xf7 [25...♖xe1 26.♖xe1
♖xe1 27.♕g8++-] **26.♖xe8+ ♕b8
27.♖xb8+ ♔xb8 28.f3** +-

(159)

▷ A. Riazantsev
► P. Harikrishna
Geneva FIDE GP, 06.07.2017

65...♕h4+! 66.g3 [66.♔e2 ♕g3–+]
**66...♕xh3 67.♕f8+ ♘d8 68.♕h8
♕xh8 69.♗xh8 ♘b7** –+

(160)

▷ O. Noroozi
► P. Darini
Asia zt Teheran, 06.07.2017

29.♖xd4! cxd4 30.♗h6 1–0[30.♗h6
♖g8 31.♗g7+ ♖xg7 32.♖b8+ ♖g8
33.♖xg8#]

(161)

▷ K. Grigoryan
► K. Ojas
Barbera del Valles Open, 06.07.2017

23.♖xc7! ♗xc7 24.♗xc7 ♘c4
25.♗xd8 ♖xd8 26.♘xc4 dxc4
27.♔f3 ♖xd4 28.♔e3 ♖d1 [28...♖d7
29.♖d2 ♖e7+ 30.♔d4+-] 29.♖d2 1–0
[29.♖d2 ♖xd2 30.♔xd2 ♔f8 31.♔c3
♔e7 32.♔xc4+-]

(162)

▷ S. Mamedyarov
► E. Inarkiev
Fide GP Geneva, 07.07.2017

20.♘h4! 1–0

(163)

▷ A. Konstantinov
► V. Sanal
Paracin Summer Open, 07.07.2017

28...♖xc8! 29.♕xe5 ♖c1 0–1 [29...♖c1
30.♖f1 ♕a1 31.♕b8+ ♔h7 32.♖xc1
♕xc1+ 33.♔h2 ♘g4+ 34.♔h3 ♘xf2+
35.♔h4 ♕h1#]

(164)

▷ L. Trent
► N. Lubbe
Lueneburg GM, 08.07.2017

29...♕d7! 0–1

(165)

▷ D. Sadzikowski
► A. David
Greek League, 08.07.2017

25.♗xa6! ♗a8 [25...♗xa6 26.♘d5
♕c5 27.♘f6+ ♔f8 28.♘xh7+ ♔g8
29.♘f6+ ♔f8 30.♕h8#] 26.♗b5±

(166)

▷ A. Kovacevic
► E. Tanriverdi
Paracin Summer Open, 08.07.2017

16.♘f6+! gxf6 17.♗xg6 fxg6
18.♕xg6+ ♔h8 [18...♗g7 19.♖g3 ♖e7
20.exf6 ♖f7 21.♗d4+-] 19.♖g3 1–0

(167)

▷ D. Kollars
► P. Keyser
Lueneburg Open, 08.07.2017

15.♕xg6+! 1–0 [15.♕xg6+ hxg6
16.♖xh8+ ♔d7 17.♖h7++-]

(168)

▷ A. Gupta
► S. Vaibhav
Commonwealth Championship
New Delhi, 08.07.2017

23.♘e6+! fxe6 [23...♔g8 24.♘c7 ♖f8
25.a3+-] 24.♖f4 ♕xf4 25.gxf4 +-

(169)

▷ T. Kantans
▶ P. Prohaszka
Benasque Open, 10.07.2017

40.♖d7! ♕a8 [40...♖f8 41.♕a7+-]
41.♕d6 ♔h8 42.♘xe6 ♖g8 43.♘xg7
♕e4 **44.♕h6+ ♗h7 45.♕f6** +-

(170)

▷ S. Salem
▶ Y. Hou
Geneva FIDE GP, 12.07.2017

30...♘e2! 31.♖f3 [31.♖d3 ♕e5+-+]
31...♖xf3 0–1

(171)

▷ D. Vocaturo
▶ P. Prohaszka
Benasque Open, 13.07.2017

32...♘g3! 0–1

(172)

▷ J. Soyer
▶ N. Maiorov
Vaujany Open, 13.07.2017

15...♕c7! 0–1

(173)

▷ A. Kovacevic
▶ I. Can
Paracin Summer Open, 14.07.2017

27...♕xe3! 0–1 [27...♕xe3 28.fxe3
♖xg2+ 29.♔h1 ♖g4+ 30.♘d5 ♗xd5+
31.♖xd5 ♖xh4–+]

(174)

▷ A. Mokshanov
▶ V. Belous
Samara Polugaevsky Memorial,
15.07.2017

22...♖f8! 23.♔d1 ♘e3+ 0–1 [23...
♘e3+ 24.♗xe3 ♖f1#]

(175)

▷ D. Derakhshani
▶ F. Rambaldi
Bergamo Open, 15.07.2017

21...♖xe2+! 0–1 [21...♖xe2+ 22.♔xe2
(22.♘xe2 ♖xh5–+) 22...♘f4+-+]

(176)

▷ A. Naiditsch
▶ R. Ponomariov
Danzhou, 17.07.2017

52.g6+! ♔h8 [52...♔h6 53.♕c1++-]
53.h6 gxh6 [53...♖e2 54.hxg7+ (54.
h7?? ♖e5+ 55.♔xe5=) 54...♔xg7
55.♕c3++-] **54.♕c3+ ♖g7 55.♔g4!**
♘e7 **56.♔h5 ♔g8** [56...♘g8 57.♕e5
♘e7 58.♔xh6+-] **57.♕b3+ ♔h8**
58.♕b8+ ♘g8 59.♕b2 1–0

(177)

▷ V. Georgiev
► S. Gauri
Dayton Masters, 18.07.2017

24.♗c6! [24.♘c6 ♛g5 25.f4+−]
24...♗xc6 25.♘xc6 ♛e6 [25...♘c7
26.♘e7++−] 26.♛xd5 1−0

(178)

▷ P. Schlosser
► R. Vogel
Pardubice Open Rapid, 20.07.2017

16...♘xf2!! 17.♔xf2 fxe5 18.♗xf5
♖xf5+ 19.♔g1 ♛c2! 20.♛xc2 ♘xc2
21.♖c1 ♘xe3 22.dxe5 ♖af8 −+

(179)

▷ S. Dvoirys
► M. Manik
Pardubice Open, 20.07.2017

29...♖xg4+! 0−1 [29...♖xg4+ 30.fxg4
♛xf1+ 31.♔h2 ♖f2+ 32.♛xf2 ♘xg4#]

(180)

▷ M. Parligras
► A. Demchenko
Turkish League, 21.07.2017

35.♖g8+! ♔xh7 36.♛g2 ♖g4 [36...
♛f6 37.♖h1++−] 37.♛xg4 1−0

(181)

▷ G. Gopal
► J. Vykouk
Pardubice Open, 23.07.2017

23.♗h7+! ♔xh7 24.♖xf8 ♗c6 25.f5
exf5 26.e6 f6 27.e7 1−0

(182)

▷ D. Forcen Esteban
► I. Akash Pc
Andorra Open, 26.07.2017

26.♖xe6! fxe6 27.♖e5! 1−0 [27.♖e5
♖f8 (27...g5 28.♛g6+−) 28.♘h2+−]

(183)

▷ B. Dauth
► J. Schroeder
Helsingor Xtracon Open, 26.07.2017

19.♗e2! ♘g8 [19...♔f8 20.♖f6+! gxf6
21.♗h5 ♘g6 22.♗xg6 ♛d7 23.♛h8+
♔e7 24.♖e1++−] 20.♖g6 1−0

(184)

▷ A. Seyb
► M. Antipov
Biel MTO Open, 27.07.2017

17...♖xb3!! 18.cxb3 [18.♗xe5 ♗xe5
19.♛e1 ♛xe1 20.♖hxe1 ♖b8 21.♖xe5+
♔d7−+; 18.bxc3 ♛a3+ 19.♔d2 ♖b2−+]
18...♛xa2 19.♛c2 ♛a1+ 20.♛b1
♗xb2+ 21.♔d2 ♗c3+ 22.♔e2 ♛xb1
23.♖xb1 gxf6 24.♖bc1 ♗d4 25.♖xc6
♗d7 26.♖xf6 ♔e7 0−1

(185)

▷ B. Juhasz
► M. Stojanovic
Senta Open, 27.07.2017

21...♗xe4! 22.♖xe4 ♕c5! 0–1 [22...
♕c5 23.h4 h6–+]

(186)

▷ Y. Wen
► X. Xu
Chinese League, 28.07.2017

30...♖c7!! 31.♕a3 [31.♖xc7 ♕xe1+
32.♔h2 ♗e5+–+] 31...a5 [31...♗b2∓]
32.g3 ♗b2 33.♕xb2 ♕xb2 34.♖xc7
♕b1 35.♔f1∓

(187)

▷ A. Kvon
► F. Svane
Helsingor Xtracon Open, 29.07.2017

19.♖xf7+!! ♔xf7 20.♕g6+ ♔e7
21.♕xg7+ ♔d6 22.♘e4+ ♔d5
23.♕g5+ e5 24.♘c3+ ♔c4 25.♗g8+
♔b4 26.a3+ ♔a5 27.b4+ ♘xb4
28.axb4+ ♔xb4 29.♘d5+ ♖xd5
30.♖b1+ 1–0

(188)

▷ M. Kravtsiv
► I. Rozum
Turkish League, 30.07.2017

30.♗xf7+! ♔xf7 [30...♖xf7
31.♕xe6+–; 30...♔h7 31.♗g6+
♔xg6 32.♕xe6++–] 31.♕d7+

♔g6 32.♕xe6+ ♔h7 33.♕g4 ♖f8
34.♕xe4+ ♔h8 35.d5 ♕d2 36.♖f1
1–0

(189)

▷ Y. Hou
► E. Bacrot
Biel GM, 31.07.2017

36.♖e5! 1–0[36.♖e5 ♖d7 (36...♕h7
37.♕g5++–; 36...♕f8 37.♖g5++–)
37.♖g5+–]

(190)

▷ V. Dragnev
► P. Vishnu
Biel MTO Open, 01.08.2017

25...♖xf1+!! [25...♕f5 26.♗d3 ♕g4–
+] 26.♖xf1 ♘e2+ 0–1

(191)

▷ P. Harikrishna
► E. Bacrot
Biel GM, 02.08.2017

21...♗xf5! 22.♘xf5 [22.♕xf5 ♖d5–+]
22...♕h2+ 23.♔f1 ♖d2 24.f4 h5
25.♕f3 ♕h1+ 26.♗g1 ♗a7 27.♖e3
♗xe3 28.♘xe3 ♖e8 29.♘c4 ♖c2 0–1

(192)

▷ L. Aronian
► F. Caruana
Sinquefield Cup Saint Louis,
03.08.2017

33...♗b4! 34.♖c1 ♖e8 35.f4 f6 36.♖c7+ ♔h8 37.♖c6 fxe5 38.♖xb6 exf4+ –+

(193)

▷ M. Kravtsiv
► S. Zhigalko
Turkish League, 04.08.2017

31.♘xf7! ♕d7 [31...♔xf7 32.♕f5+ ♔e7 33.♗xd5 ♖f8 34.♕xe6+ ♕xe6 35.♗xe6 ♔xe6 36.♖xc6+ ♔d5 37.♖c7+-] **32.♘e5 +-**

(194)

▷ N. Grandelius
► D. Yuffa
Lund CellaVision Cup, 06.08.2017

24.♖b7+! ♔c6 [24...♔c8 25.♖b6+ ♔c7 26.♖xe6+-] **25.♖c1+ ♔d6 26.♖b6+ ♔d7 27.♗b5+ 1–0**[27.♗b5+ ♔e7 28.♖xe6+ ♔xe6 29.♗c4++-]

(195)

▷ J. Ehlvest
► A. Neiksans
Liepajas Rokade Rapid, 06.08.2017

25...♘e2+! 26.♗xe2 [26.♖xe2 ♗xe2–+; 26.♔h1 ♕xf2–+] **26...**

♕xf2+ 27.♔h1 ♖xe3 28.♖f1 ♖xe2 29.♖xf2 ♖fxf2 0–1

(196)

▷ V. Jianu
► C. Voiteanu
Arad Open, 07.08.2017

26.♘xf7! 1–0 [26.♘xf7 ♖xd2 27.♘h6+ ♔h8 28.♕g8+ ♖xg8 29.♘f7#]

(197)

▷ P. Salinas Herrera
► K. Grigoryan
Badalona Open, 09.08.2017

21...♗b5! 0–1[21...♗b5 22.♗xd5 (22. ♖f2 ♖e1+–+; 22.♖f3 ♗c5+–+) 22... ♗xf1 23.♖xe4 ♗e2! 24.♖d4 ♗c5–+]

(198)

▷ D. Miedema
► D. Kryakvin
Riga Tech Open, 09.08.2017

20...♖xf2+! 21.♔d1 [21.♗xf2 ♘f4+–+] **21...♘xb2+ 22.♔c1 ♘d3+ 23.♔d1 ♕f8 24.♕xe4 ♖e8 0–1**

(199)

▷ C. Ali Marandi
► T. Kaasen
Riga Tech open, 11.08.2017

22.♖dh1!! f5 [22...♕xb2+ 23.♔d2 c3+ (23...♗xe5 24.♗xe5 ♕xe5 25.♕h8+

♕xh8 26.♖xh8+ ♔g7 27.♖1h7#)
24.♔e2 ♕xc2+ 25.♔f1 ♕b1+
26.♔g2+-] **23.exf6 exf6 24.♕h8+**
1-0[24.♕h8+ ♔f7 25.♕xg7+
♔xg7 26.♖h7+ ♔f8 27.♖h8+ ♔e7
28.♖1h7#]

(200)

▷ **D. Alsina Leal**
► **F. Podvin**
Spaish Championship Rapid Lin-
ares, 13.08.2017

21...♖d8! 22.♖e1 [22.♖xd8 ♕xd8
23.♕xa7+ ♔g8 24.h3 ♕d1+ 25.♔h2
♕e2 26.♕g1 ♗xh3–+] **22...♖d5**
23.♕xc6 ♕xa5 –+

(201)

▷ **A. Alonso Rosell**
► **F. Garcia Molina**
Spanish Championship Rapid Lin-
ares, 13.08.2017

17.♕g4! ♗c8 [17...♖ad8 18.♗g5+-;
17...♕d8 18.♗h6+-] **18.♗g5 ♕d6**
19.♕h4 [19.♗e7+-] **19...f5 20.♗e7** +-

(202)

▷ **Q. Le**
► **F. Caruana**
Saint Louis Rapid, 14.08.2017

50...♔e8?? [50...♖f2! 51.♖g8+ ♔e7
52.♖a8 ♕b6–+] **51.♖a7** [51.♖g8+!
♔d7 52.♖6g7+ ♔c6 53.♖c8+ ♔b6
54.♖b8++-] **51...♔f8 52.♖a8+ ♔f7**
53.♖ag8 1-0

(203)

▷ **A. Indjic**
► **L. Vogt**
Abu Dhabi Open, 15.08.2017

26.♘f8! 1-0 [26.♘f8 ♕xe7 27.♘xg6+
♔h7 28.♘xe7+-]

(204)

▷ **A. Leniart**
► **M. Bartel**
Suwalki Warakomska Memorial,
16.08.2017

19.♖f3! ♖f6 [19...♘f6 20.♘g6+ hxg6
21.♖h3+ ♘h7 22.fxg6+-] **20.♘g6+**
♖xg6 [20...hxg6 21.♖h3#] **21.fxg6**
♘f6 22.♕e6 +-

(205)

▷ **S. Karjakin**
► **V. Anand**
Saint Louis Rapid, 16.08.2017

37.♕c6! 1-0 [37.♕c6 ♖xd6 (37...
♘f8 38.♖xh6+ gxh6 39.♕xh6+ ♔g8
40.♕g5+ ♔h8 41.♗e5++-) 38.♕xa8+
♔h7 39.♗xd6+-]

(206)

▷ **N. Grandelius**
► **D. Forcen Esteban**
Spanish League, 17.08.2017

15.♘xe6!! [15.a4+-] **15...♘xe6**
16.♘d5 ♕b8 17.♖f7 1-0[17.♖f7 ♘e7
18.♗g4+-]

(207)

▷ H. Nakamura
► V. Anand
Saint Louis Blitz, 18.08.2017

51.♖xf7+! ♕xf7 52.♕h8+ 1–0[52. ♕h8+ ♔e7 53.♕xd4+–]

(208)

▷ J. Maia
► L. Krysa
Barcelona Sants Open, 18.08.2017

18...♕b4+! 0–1[18...♕b4+ 19.♕d2 (19. ♔f1 ♕b5+ 20.♔e1 (20.♔g1 ♖g4#) 20... ♖e4+–+) 19...♖e4+ 20.♔d1 ♖d4–+]

(209)

▷ C. Li
► Q. Ma
Chinese League, 18.08.2017

47.♖xg6+! ♕xg6 [47...♔f5 48.♖g8+ ♔e6 49.♖e8++–] **48.f4+** [48.♕h4+ ♔f5 49.♕e4+ ♔g5 50.♕f4+ ♔h5 51.♕h4#] **48...♔f5 49.g4+ ♔xf4 50.♕xg6 ♖d6 51.♕f5+** 1–0

(210)

▷ A. Tahay
► L. Krysa
Barcelona Sants Open, 20.08.2017

25...e3! 26.♖e2 [26.♘xe3 ♖xe3 27.♕xg6 ♖xe1+ 28.♖xe1 hxg6–+] **26...exf2+ 27.♖xf2 ♗g3 28.♖xf8+ ♖xf8 29.♕xg6 ♗f2+** 0–1

(211)

▷ E. Blomqvist
► M. Kleinman
Barcelona Sants Open, 20.08.2017

27...♖f8! 28.♕xg6 ♖xf2+ 29.♔xf2 ♕d2+ 0–1[29...♕d2+ 30.♔g3 ♕f4+–+]

(212)

▷ I. Rozum
► D. Harika
Abu Dhabi Open, 21.08.2017

33.♕e2! g5 34.fxe3 +–

(213)

▷ A. Stukopin
► B. Macieja
US Masters Open Greensboro,
25.08.2017

27.♖e1! ♖f4? [27...♘xc4 28.e7++–; 27... ♘g6 28.b5 (28.♖d1+ ♔e8 29.♗d3 ♘e5 30.♗xh7 ♖h8 31.♖e1 ♖xh7 32.♖xe5 ♖xh3 33.♖g5 ♖xa3 34.♖xg7±) 28... ♔e7 29.bxc6 bxc6 30.♖e3±] **28.e7+ ♔e8 29.♗e6!** [29.♗e6 ♘f3 30.♗d7+ ♔xd7 31.e8♕++–]

(214)

▷ T. Kotanjian
► V. Teterev
Avicenna Open Hamedan,
27.08.2017

23... ♗h6!! 0–1 [23... ♗h6 24.♕b3 (24. ♗xh6 ♕xb6+ 25.♔h1 ♘g4–+) 24... ♗xe3+ 25.♕xe3 ♘g4–+]

[215]

▷ **V. Artemiev**
► **D. Lintchevski**
St. Petersburg Rapid, 27.08.2017

35.♖g8+! 1–0 [35.♖g8+ ♔xg8 36.♘xf6+ ♔g7 37.♘xd5+-]

[216]

▷ **J. Xiong**
► **M. Vachier Lagrave**
Internet Blitz, 30.08.2017

22... ♕xf3+! 23.gxf3 ♗h3# 0–1

[217]

▷ **K. Shevchenko**
► **A. Barp**
Trieste Open, 02.09.2017

24...♘d5!! 0–1 [24...♘d5 25.exd5 ♕h4+ 26.g3 ♕xh2#]

[218]

▷ **R. Markus**
► **D. Milanovic**
Serbian League, 03.09.2017

48.c5! bxc5 49.♕xc5 ♕xc5 [49... ♕d2+ 50.♔h3 ♔g8 51.♕e7 ♕d7 52.♕xd7 ♗xd7 53.♔g2+-] **50.♘xe6+ ♔f6 51.♘xc5** +-

[219]

▷ **V. Dobrov**
► **A. Reshetnikov**
Moscow Blitz, 03.09.2017

20.♗h6+! ♔xh6 [20...♔g8 21.♕f6+-] **21.♕f6+ ♘g6** [21...♔h5 22.g4#] **22.♖d3** 1–0

[220]

▷ **A. Dreev**
► **A. Bachmann**
Fide World Cup Tbilisi, 04.09.2017

26.♗xe6! ♖g8 [26...fxe6 27.♘g6+ ♔f6 28.♘xh8 ♔g7 29.♗xe6+-] **27.♗xf7 ♖xg3 28.♗e6+ ♔d8 29.♖d2+ ♔c7 30.♖e7+ ♔b6 31.♖d6+ ♔b5 32.♗c4+ ♔a5 33.♗e2** 1–0

[221]

▷ **Y. Wei**
► **B. Sambuev**
Fide World Cup Tbilisi, 05.09.2017

11.♗d2! ♗xd2 [11...f5 12.♘g5 ♗xd2 13.♘xe6 ♕c8 14.♘xg7+ ♔f8 15.♘e6+ ♔e8 16.♘xd7 ♕xd7 17.♘c5 ♕xd4 18.♘xb7 ♔f7 (18...♖b8 19.e3 ♕f6 20.♘c5+-) 19.e3 ♕xb2 20.axb5 axb5 21.♖b1 ♕c3 22.♗xc6! ♘xc6 23.♕h5+ ♔e7 24.♖xb5+-] **12.♘d6+ ♔f8 13.♘exf7 ♕c7 14.♕xd2 ♘c8 15.♕f4 ♘f6 16.♘xc8 ♕xf4 17.gxf4 ♖xc8 18.♘xh8** +-

[222]

▷ L. Lenic
▶ L. Fressinet
Fide World Cup Tbilisi, 05.09.2017

45.♖xf8+! ♔xf8 **46.**♗h6+ ♔e7
[46...♔g8 47.♕g5+ ♔h7 48.♔g3+–]
47.♕g5+ ♔xd6 **48.**♕d8+ ♔e5
49.♗g7+ 1–0

[223]

▷ P. Harikrishna
▶ Y. Gonzalez Vidal
Fide World Cup Tbilisi, 05.09.2017

40.♕c7+! ♗e7 [40...♔h8 41.♕b8
♕e7 (41...♔g7 42.♕b7+ ♔h8 43.♘f7+
♔g8 44.♘d8 ♗e7 45.♕d5+ ♔h8
46.♖e4 ♕c5 47.♕b3+–) 42.♖e4 ♕c5
43.♖e8 ♔g7 44.♖c8+–; 40...♗xh6
41.♖h4+ ♔g5 42.♕f4#] **41.**♘f5+
♕xf5 **42.**♕xe7+ ♔g8 **43.**♖b4
♕e5 **44.**♕d8+ ♔g7 **45.**♖b7+ ♔h6
46.♕f8+ 1–0

[224]

▷ M. Adams
▶ T. Batchuluun
Fide World Cup Tbilisi, 05.09.2017

31.♖d5+! ♔e6 [31...♔e4 32.♘c3#]
32.♘c7+ 1–0 [32.♘c7+ ♔e7
33.♖xf5+–]

[225]

▷ W. So
▶ M. Bluebaum
FIDE World Cup Tbilisi, 08.09.2017

21.♘f3! 1–0 [21.♘f3 ♕f4 22.♖xe7+–]

[226]

▷ D. Khegay
▶ I. Bocharov
Cheliabinsk Kurnosov Memorial
Rapid, 09.09.2017

19...d4! **20.**exd4 [20.♗xd4 ♗xb4+
21.♔d1 ♗c2+ 22.♔c1 ♗a4+ 23.♔b1
♗a3 24.♗b2 ♗c2+ 25.♔c1 ♗e4+
26.♔d2 ♗xb2–+] **20...**♗g5+ 0–1

[227]

▷ B. Vuckovic
▶ S. Rogac
Serbian League, 10.09.2017

18.♘xe6! ♕xe6 **19.**♕a4+ ♔e7
20.♖d6 ♕c8 **21.**♖ad1 ♖a7 **22.**♕h4+
f6 **23.**exf6+ ♔f7 **24.**♕h5+ g6
25.♕d5+ 1–0

[228]

▷ I. Lysyj
▶ A. Shariyazdanov
Cheliabinsk Kurnosov Memorial
Rapid, 10.09.2017

23.♖xf6! ♖xf6 **24.**♗d4 ♕e6 **25.**♕b4
[25.♕c3+–] **25...**a5 **26.**♕c5 ♗d7
27.♖f1 ♖af8 **28.**♕xf8+ 1–0

[229]

▷ D. Dubov
▶ V. Artemiev
Fide World Cup Tbilisi, 10.09.2017

30.♖xe8+! [30.♕xh2 ♕a2#] 30...
♔xe8 31.♕b8+ ♗c8 [31...♔e7
32.♕d8#] 32.♕xh2 ♘c3+ 33.bxc3
♕xb5+ 34.♔c1 ♕g5+ 35.♖d2 ♕a5
36.♖d4 +-

(230)

▷ A. Arribas Lopez
▶ A. Pichot
Saint Louis Fall-B, 10.09.2017

29...♖xd2!! 30.♖xd2 [30.♗xd2 b3
31.♖a1 b2 32.♗c3 bxa1♕+ 33.♗xa1
♗g5-+] 30...b3 31.♖d7 a2 0-1

(231)

▷ G. Meier
▶ V. Kovalev
Saint Louis Fall-A, 11.09.2017

38.♖e6! fxe6 39.f6 1-0

(232)

▷ A. Lenderman
▶ M. Vachier Lagrave
Fide World Cup Tbilisi, 11.09.2017

35...♖c2! 36.♖xf7 [36.e6 fxe6
37.♘xe6 d3-+] 36...♔g6 37.e6 ♖xc5
38.g4 ♘e3 39.f5+ ♔h7 40.e7 ♖e5
41.f6 ♔g6 42.♖f8 d3 43.fxg7 ♔xg7
44.♖d8 [44.e8♕ ♖xe8 45.♖xe8
d2-+] 44...♖xe7 -+

(233)

▷ B. Jobava
▶ I. Nepomniachtchi
Fide World Cup Tbilisi, 11.09.2017

33.♕xd4! 1-0[33.♘e8++-; 33.♕xd4
♖xd4 34.♘e8++-]

(234)

▷ M. Santos Ruiz
▶ A. Sousa
European Championship U18
Mamaia, 14.09.2017

28.♖xf7+! ♔xf7 29.♕b7+ ♔f6
30.♕g7# 1-0

(235)

▷ A. Kislinsky
▶ M. Bagheri
Yerevan Open, 20.09.2017

23.♘xe5!! ♘xg6 [23...♕xa2
24.♘xf7+ ♔g8 25.♘xh6+ ♔h8
26.♕h5 gxh6 27.♗xh6 ♕d5 28.♗g7+!
♔g8 29.♕h8+ ♔f7 30.♗xf8+-]
24.♘xg6+ 1-0

(236)

▷ D. Shengelia
▶ B. Bellahcene
Mitropa Cup Balatonszarszo,
25.09.2017

18...♖xf2!! 19.♗f3 [19.h3 ♖xg2+
20.♔xg2 ♘e3+-+; 19.♕d2 ♖xg2+
20.♔xg2 ♗xe4+-+; 19.♗h3 e5-+]
19...♕h6 20.h4 ♕e3 21.♖d3 ♖xf3+

22.♖xe3 ♖xe3 23.♘g5 ♖xg3+ 24.♔f1 ♘e3+ 0–1

(237)

▷ Q. Le
► Y. Wang
Asian Team Championship Rapid
Ashkhabad, 25.09.2017

40.♕xc6 1–0 [40.♕xc6 ♕xc6 41.d7+-]

(238)

▷ R. Hovhannishyan
► A. Moskalenko
Yerevan Open, 25.09.2017

34.♖xa7+! 1–0 [34.♖xa7+ ♔xa7 35.♕a3+ ♔b7 36.♕a6#]

(239)

▷ R. Hovhannishyan
► M. Tabatabaei
Yerevan Open, 27.09.2017

24...♖xf3! [24...♘xf3+ 25.♖xf3 ♕xe4-+] 25.♖xf3 ♕xe4 26.♘d2 ♕xd4+ 27.♔f1 ♘xf3 28.♘xf3 ♕xg4 29.h3 ♕xh3+ 30.♔f2 ♖f8 –+

(240)

▷ L. Ding
► L. Aronian
Fide World Cup Tbilisi, 27.09.2017

31...♕h4! 32.♖e8+ [32.♖xf5 ♕xh2#] 32...♔g7 33.♖g1+ ♔f6 0–1

(241)

▷ A. Jakubiec
► M. Krasenkow
Polish League, 29.09.2017

35...♘c3+! [35...♕xc2+ 36.♔xc2 ♘d4+ 37.♔b1 ♘xc6 38.♖xe4∓] 36.bxc3 ♖b8+ 37.♕b5 ♖xb5+ 38.cxb5 ♕d5 39.♘d4 ♗xd4 40.cxd4 ♕xb5+ 0–1

(242)

▷ I. Sokolov
► R. Rapport
Douglas IoM Open, 30.09.2017

31...♘xg2 0–1

(243)

▷ D. Howell
► J. Timman
Douglas IoM Open, 30.09.2017

42.♘xe6 1–0 [42.♘xe6 fxe6 (42... ♖xc1 43.♕g7#) 43.♖xc8++-]

(244)

▷ Z. Tsydypov
► A. Sorokin
Russian Championship Rapid Sochi, 01.10.2017

26.♘h5+! ♔h8 [26...gxh5 27.♕g5+ ♔h8 28.♕f5 ♘f6 29.♕xf6+ ♔g8 30.♕g5+ ♔h8 31.♕f5+-] 27.♗xg6 ♖g8 [27...fxg6 28.♕d4+ ♘f6 29.♘xf6+-] 28.♗xf7 ♘f6 29.♖xc8 ♕xc8 30.♗xg8 1–0

(245)

▷ V. Anand
► Y. Hou
Douglas IoM open, 01.10.2017

25.♘xf7! ♖xe3 [25...♔xf7 26.♖xe8
♕xe8 27.♕f5+ ♔g8 28.♖xe8+ ♖xe8
29.♕xf4+-] **26.♖xe3 ♔xf7** [26...
♘xh3+ 27.gxh3 ♔xf7 28.♕h7+-]
27.♖f3 ♔g8 [27...g5 28.♕h7+ ♔e8
29.g3 ♕xh3 30.♖e3+ ♘e6 31.♕g8++-]
**28.♖xf4 ♕e6 29.♕f5 ♖e8 30.♕xe6+
♖xe6 31.♔f1 î S**

(246)

▷ M. Demidov
► A. Korotylev
Russian Championship Blitz Sochi,
02.10.2017

24.♘xe5! ♖xd5 [24...♘xe5 25.♖xc5+-]
25.♘xd7 b5 [25...g5 26.♕c2±] **26.♕c2
g5 27.♕c8+ ♕xc8 28.♘f6+ ♔g7
29.♘xh5+ ♔g6 30.♖xc8 ♔xh5
31.♖a8 1-0**

(247)

▷ O. Girya
► E. Ovod
Russian League Rapid, 03.10.2017

24.♘e5! ♖b7 [24...♘xe5 25.♖d8++-]
25.♘e7+ ♔f8 [25...♔h8 26.♘xf7#]
26.♕c8+ ♔xe7 [26...♘e8 27.♘7c6
♘xe5 28.♕xe8+ ♔xe8 29.♖d8#]
27.♘c6# 1-0

(248)

▷ S. Feller
► Z. Medvegy
Croatian League Mali Losinj,
03.10.2017

24.♖xc6! 1-0 [24.♖xc6 ♖xd1
25.♖xc8++-]

(249)

▷ V. Artemiev
► A. Morozevich
Russian League Rapid, 04.10.2017

20.♖xh6! 1-0 [20.♖xh6 ♔xh6
21.♖h1+ ♔g7 22.♖h7++-]

(250)

▷ M. Lagarde
► V. Fedoseev
European Club Cup Antalya,
09.10.2017

37...♖g4! 38.♖d1 ♖h4 39.♖xe3 [39.
♘xe3 ♕h1+ 40.♔f2 ♖xf4+ 41.♔e1
♖xf1+ 42.♘xf1 ♕h4+-+] **39...♕h2+
0-1** [39...♕h2+ 40.♔f2 ♖xf4+-+]

(251)

▷ H. Steingrimsson
► Z. Efimenko
European Club Cup Antalya,
10.10.2017

46...♖b1!! 47.♕e5+ [47.♖xb1 ♕xf2+
48.♔h1 ♕h2#] **47...♔h7 48.♕e7
♕xf1+ 49.♔xg3 ♕g1+ 50.♔f3 ♕h1+**
0-1

(252)

▷ A. Naiditsch
► V. Kramnik
European Club Cup Antalya,
12.10.2017

36.♕c7! ♖g8 37.♘d3 ♕e4 38.♘xf4+-

(253)

▷ C. Li
► L. Shytaj
French League, 22.10.2017

22.♘xf7! ♖xd4 [22...♔xf7 23.♕xe6+
♔g6 24.♗c2+ ♔h5 25.♕h3+ ♔g5
26.f4#] 23.♘xh6+ gxh6 24.♕xa8+
♖d8 25.♕e4 1-0

(254)

▷ N. Dzagnidze
► O. Girya
European Championship Rapid Monaco, 22.10.2017

21...♘xh2! 22.♘xh2 [22.♖xg8
♘xf3+ 23.♔e2 ♕xg8 24.♔xf3 ♕g4#]
22...♖xg1+ -+

(255)

▷ V. Gunina
► A. Kosteniuk
European Championship Blitz Monaco, 23.10.2017

93...♕e6+! 94.♔xh5 ♔h7 0-1[94...
♔h7 95.♕f4 (95.♕g4 ♕h6#) 95...
♕g6#]

(256)

▷ P. Tregubov
► J. Moussard
Corsica Masters Bastia Rapid,
26.10.2017

27...♕xf3! 28.♕xe5+ [28.♗xf3
♘d3+-+] 28...f6 29.♕e7 ♖g1+
30.♔d2 ♕f4+ 31.♔c2 ♕c1# 0-1

(257)

▷ V. Onischuk
► A. Puranik
Corsica Masters Open Bastia,
26.10.2017

16.♗xh6! gxh6 17.♕xh6 ♖e7 [17...
♕e7 18.♗xe6 ♕xe6 19.♘f5+-]
18.♗xe6 ♖xe6 19.♘g5 ♕d7 20.♘f5
♘e8 21.♗e3 1-0[21.♗e3 ♖f6 22.♖g3
♖xf5 23.exf5 ♕xf5 24.♕h7+ ♔f8
25.♖f3+-]

(258)

▷ C. Repka
► M. Bartel
European Team Championship
Crete, 28.10.2017

31.♖xf7!! ♘c5 [31...♖xc2 32.♗b7+
♔b8 33.♖xd8+ ♖c8 34.♖xc8#; 31...
♘c3+ 32.♕xc3 ♕xc3 33.bxc3 ♖xf7
34.♗e6+! ♔c7 35.♖xd8 ♔xd8
36.♗xf7+-] 32.♕xg6 ♖xf7 33.♕c6+
♖c7 34.♗e6+ ♘d7 35.♕a8# 1-0

(259)

▷ D. Navara
▶ A. Rasmussen
European Team Championship
Crete, 28.10.2017

38.♖xe6!! ♘h6+ [38...fxe6 39.♘xe6+
♔g8 40.♘xf8+-] **39.♖xh6! ♔xh6
40.♔f5 ♔xh5 41.f4** 1–0[41.f4 ♔h4
42.♔f6+-]

(260)

▷ A. Giri
▶ P. Eljanov
European Team Championship
Crete, 29.10.2017

**34.♖xe6! ♖xe6 35.♕xf5 g6 36.♕xe6
♕xe6 37.♖xe6 ♘xc3 38.♖xg6** 1–0

(261)

▷ V. Artemiev
▶ A. Sarana
Chigorin Memorial St. Petersburg,
29.10.2017

57...♖e6! [57...gxf4+ 58.♔xf4
♖xd4+–+] **58.f5+ ♔f6** 0–1[58...♔f6
59.fxe6 ♔xe7 60.exf7 a5–+]

(262)

▷ L. Paichadze
▶ G. Kjartansson
European Team Championship
Crete, 30.10.2017

27.♗e3! d4 28.♘xd4 ♗c5 [28...exd4
29.♗xd4 b6 30.♕e4+ ♕b7 31.♕xb7+

♔xb7 32.♖xb6++-] **29.♘e6** 1–0[29.
♘e6 ♗xe3 30.♘c7#]

(263)

▷ A. Fedorov
▶ J. Skoberne
European Team Championship
Crete, 30.10.2017

18.♘f5+! ♔h8 [18...gxf5 19.♕g3++-]
**19.♕xc6 ♕b6 20.♕xb6 ♘xb6
21.hxg6 fxg6 22.♘d6** +-

(264)

▷ S. Mamedyarov
▶ D. Svetushkin
European Team Championship
Crete, 31.10.2017

26.♗xf5! e3 [26...gxf5 27.♕g5+
♔h8 28.♕f6+ ♔g8 29.♕f7+ ♔h8
30.♕xh7#; 26...♖f3 27.♕h4 ♗g7
28.♗xe4 ♕xb4 29.♖d1+-] **27.♗xg6!
♕xf4 28.♗f7+ ♔h8 29.gxf4 ♗xb4
30.♖xe3 ♖e7 31.♖xb5 ♗d6 32.♖xa3
♗xa3 33.♖g5 h6 34.♖g6** 1–0

(265)

▷ A. Demuth
▶ A. Savina
Karpov Trophy Cape d'Age Blitz,
31.10.2017

**20.♘xe6! ♔xe6 21.♗xb6 axb6
22.♗c4+ ♔e5 23.♖d5+ ♔e6 24.♖d4+**
1–0[24.♖d4+ ♔e5 25.f4#]

(266)

▷ G. Kjartansson
► M. Sebenik
European Team Championship
Crete, 01.11.2017

24...♖d2+! 25.♔xd2 [25.♗xd2 ♘xc4–+] 25...♘xc4+ 26.♔d3 ♘xb2+ 27.♔e2 ♕d8 28.♗e4 ♖e8 29.♔f3 ♖xe4 0–1

(267)

▷ A. Demuth
► A. Pourramezanali
Karpov Trophy Cap d'Agde Rapid,
01.11.2017

46.♗d3+! ♔h8 [46...g6 47.hxg6+ ♔h8 48.♕e8+ ♘g8 49.♕f7 ♗g7 50.e7+–] 47.♕e8+ ♘g8 48.♕g6 +–

(268)

▷ C. Aravindh
► S. Swapnil
Indian Championship Patna,
01.11.2017

50.♖xa7!! ♖xa7 51.axb6 ♖a8 [51... ♖b7 52.♔c5 ♖b8 53.♔c6 ♖c8+ 54.♔d6+–] 52.♔c5 ♔e7 53.b7 ♖d8 54.♔c6 ♔e8 55.♔c7 ♖d7+ 56.♔b6 ♖d8 57.♔a7 ♖d7 58.♔a8 1–0

(269)

▷ Z. Almasi
► H. Stevic
European Team Championship
Crete, 03.11.2017

29.♖c1! ♕d6 [29...♕xd5 30.♖e8++–] 30.♘c7 ♖ac8 31.♘b5 [31.♖xf7 ♕xd4 32.♘e6 ♖xc1 33.♖xc1+–] 31...♕b4 32.b3 +–

(270)

▷ A. Ramirez
► A. Alvarez Pedraza
Chess Rumble Panama City Rapid,
04.11.2017

24.♕xh7+! 1–0 [24.♕xh7+ ♔xh7 25.♖h4+ ♗h6 26.♖xh6+ ♔g8 27.♖h8#]

(271)

▷ A. Ushenina
► A. Matnadze
European Team Championship
Crete, 05.11.2017

30...♕xe3+!! 31.♔xe3 ♖f3+ 0–1

(272)

▷ I. Salgado Lopez
► M. Mchedlishvili
European Team Championship
Crete, 05.11.2017

34.♕g8+! 1–0 [34.♕g8+ ♔xg8 35.♘xf6+ ♔f8 36.♘xd5+–]

(273)

▷ H. Gabuzyan
► N. Sedlak
European Team Championship
Crete, 06.11.2017

43...h3! 44.♖g1 ♖c1 0–1[44...♖c1
45.♖xc1 ♕g2#]

(274)

▷ S. Bogner
► S. Brunello
European Team Championship
Crete, 06.11.2017

24.♗h7+! ♔xh7 25.♕xf8 ♘e5
26.♕b4 +-

(275)

▷ D. Fridman
► S. Ernst
Bundesliga, 12.11.2017

20.♘xe6! ♖xd1 [20...fxe6
21.♕xe6++-] 21.♖xd1 ♘xe3 22.fxe3
♗c6 [22...fxe6 23.♕xe6+ ♔f8 24.♖f1+
♗f6 25.♕d6++-] 23.♘d4 a5 24.♘d5±

(276)

▷ S. Bromberger
► A. Horvath
Bundesliga, 12.11.2017

35...♖xh2!! 0–1[35...♕a3–+; 35...
♖xh2 36.♖xc3 (36.♘xh2 ♕e1+–+;
36.♘d2 ♕xc2–+) 36...♖h1+–+]

(277)

▷ I. Barreto
► D. Lima
Duchamp Open Rio de Janeiro,
17.11.2017

19...♘xe4! 20.♘xe4 ♗xd5 21.♖c4
[21.♕d2 ♗xe4–+] 21...b5 22.♘df2
♗xc4 23.♕d2 ♘f5 0–1

(278)

▷ W. So
► M. Carlsen
Internet Blitz, 18.11.2017

58.♖c5! [58.♖a2? ♔e4 59.a8♕ ♗xa8
60.♖xa8 e2 61.♖a1 ♔f3 62.♔d6
♔f2=] 58...e2 59.♖xd5+ [59.a8♕ e1♕
60.♖xd5+ exd5 61.♕e8++-] 59...exd5
60.a8♕ ♔e4 [60...e1♕ 61.♕e8++-]
61.♔d6 1–0

(279)

▷ W. So
► M. Carlsen
Internet Blitz, 18.11.2017

29...♕xf2!! 30.♕e1 [30.♖xf2
♖d1+–+] 30...♘g3+ 0–1[30...♘g3+
31.hxg3 ♖h5#]

(280)

▷ A. Kveinys
► B. Amin
Latvian League, 18.11.2017

47...♕xg3+! 0–1 [47...♕xg3+ 48.♔xg3
♘xe4+–+]

(281)

▷ J. Sadorra
► A. Hambleton
Saint Louis GM Invitational,
19.11.2017

67.♖xg6+! ♔xg6 [67...fxg6 68.♖h7+ ♔xh7=] **68.♖d6+** ♔f5 [68...f6 69.♖xf6+=] **69.♖d5+** ♔f6 **70.♖d6+** ♔e5 **71.♖d5+** ♔xd5 ½

(282)

▷ L. Aronian
► A. Giri
Palma De Mallorca GP, 19.11.2017

25.♗h6+! ♔e8 **26.♖g8+** ♔d7 **27.d6** 1–0 [27.d6 ♕xd6 28.♖d1+–]

(283)

▷ E. Tomashevsky
► T. Radjabov
Palma De Mallorca GP, 22.11.2017

58.b5! 1–0 [58.b5 axb5 (*58...♖a7 59.axb6 ♗xb6 60.bxa6 ♖xa6 61.♗c4+–*) 59.a6 ♖a7 60.♗b7+–]

(284)

▷ A. Riazantsev
► R. Rapport
Palma De Mallorca GP, 22.11.2017

35...♘g5!! **36.♗g2** [36.♘xd7 ♘f3+ 37.♔h1 ♖h2#] **36...♗h3!** **37.♗xh3** [37.♗h1 ♗g4 38.♘d3 (*38.a6 ♖f2 39.♗g2 ♗f3 40.♗f1 (40.a7 ♖xg2+ 41.♔f1 ♘h3–+) 40...♗xe4–+ 41.♘xe4*

♘f3+ 42.♔h1 ♖h2#) 38...♘h3+ 39.♔f1 ♖h2–+] **37...♘f3+** 0–1

(285)

▷ D. Bocharov
► D. Kokarev
Ugra Governor's Cup Blitz,
22.11.2017

28.♖xe7! ♕g6 [28...♕xe7 29.♖xe7+–] **29.♖e8+** ♕xe8 [29...♔f7 30.♖1e7+ ♔f6 31.♕h4++–] **30.♕f6+** ♕f7 **31.♕d8+** 1–0

(286)

▷ P. Eljanov
► J. Hammer
Palma De Mallorca GP, 23.11.2017

25.♕xg7+! 1–0 [25.♕xg7+ ♔xg7 26.♘f5+ ♔f6 27.♘xe3 ♘xg3+ 28.♔f2 ♘xh1+ 29.♖xh1+–]

(287)

▷ A. Gilevych
► A. Stella
Italian Championship Cosenza,
29.11.2017

19...♖xd5! **20.♕xd5** ♖d8 0–1 [20... ♖d8 21.♕c6 ♕e5 22.♕xa6 ♕xa1+–+]

(288)

▷ M. Bosiocic
► S. Shyam
Tsaghkadzor Open, 01.12.2017

31...♕g1+! 32.♔e2 gxf3+ 33.♔xf3 [33.♔d2 ♕g2+−+] 33...♘h4+ 34.♔e2 ♗g4+ 35.♔d2 ♕g2+ 0–1

(289)

▷ S. Maze
▶ G. Stany
London Classic Open, 08.12.2017

30.♕xg6+!! [30.♖xd3 ♕e4 31.♖d1 ♕xc4−+] 30...♗g7 [30...♖g7 31.♕xd3+−] 31.♖xh7 ♕xg2+ 32.♖xg2 ♖dd7 33.♖h3 ♖d4 34.♖h8+ 1–0

(290)

▷ A. Graf
▶ V. Babula
Bundesliga, 10.12.2017

27...♖xe5! 28.♕xe5 ♕xc4 −+

(291)

▷ D. Dvirnyy
▶ S. Brunello
Italian Championship Cosenza,
10.12.2017

30...♖xe5! 31.♕h3 [31.♖xg6 ♗xh4 32.fxe5 hxg6−+] 31...fxe4 32.♕xd7 ♖e7 0–1

(292)

▷ M. Carlsen
▶ I. Nepomniachtchi
London Classic, 10.12.2017

36...♕a4! 37.♕xa4 [37.♕xb6 ♕xf4+−+] 37...♘xa4 38.c6 ♘b6 39.c7 f6 40.♖b3 ♘c8 0–1

(293)

▷ K. Grigoryan
▶ N. Norbaev
Johor Open, 12.12.2017

20.♖b7! [20.♖fc1+−] 20...♗xb7 21.cxb7 ♕xc5 [21...♕xb7 22.♗b5++−] 22.bxa8♕+ ♔e7 23.♕xh8 ♘f6 24.♘e5 ♕c7 25.♗b5 1–0

(294)

▷ A. Krstulovic
▶ V. Malakhatko
Zadar Open Blitz, 13.12.2017

29...♖g2+! 30.♔h1 [30.♔f1 ♖c2+−+] 30...♖c2 0–1 [30...♖c2 31.♖d8+ ♔g7 32.♗f3 ♖f2−+]

(295)

▷ B. Gledura
▶ A. Indjic
Hetenyi Geza Memorial GM Budapest, 15.12.2017

15.♗xd5! f5 [15...♘xd5 16.♘de4 ♕e6 17.♘xd5 ♕xd5 (17...♕xe4 18.♘f6++−) 18.♘f6++−] 16.♘c4 ♕f6 17.♘e5 +−

(296)

▷ A. Horvath
▶ I. Leventic
Hungarian League, 17.12.2017

1.♕xe5‼ 1–0[1.♕xg6 ♖g8 2.♕f5+–;
1.♕xe5 ♕xe5 (1...♔g8 2.♖xg6++–)
2.♖f8+ ♖xf8 3.♖xf8#]

(297)

▷ O. Almeida Quintana
▶ A. Gorovets
Carlos Torre Memorial Merida,
17.12.2017

36.♕h8+! ♔g5 37.f4+ 1–0[37.f4+ ♔f5
(37...♔g4 38.♕h3#) 38.♕e5+ ♔g4
39.♕g5#]

(298)

▷ S. Nihal
▶ R. Zhalmakhanov
World Youth U16 Olympiad,
18.12.2017

29.♘b6! 1–0[29.♘b6 ♘xb6 (29...
♖xc2 30.♘xc8++–) 30.♖xc7++–]

(299)

▷ Z. Medvegy
▶ T. Banusz
Hetenyi Geza Memorial GM Budapest, 20.12.2017

32...♘f5! 33.♔e2 [33.♗e1 ♘e7–+]
33...♘xh4 34.♔f2 [34.g3 ♘f5∓] 34...
♘f5 35.♗d2 ♘e7∓

(300)

▷ S. Mamedyarov
▶ D. Yuffa
Nutcracker Classical Moscow,
21.12.2017

27.♖xg6+! ♔xg6 28.♘e5+ 1–0 [28.
♘e5+ ♔f5 (28...♕xe5 29.♕xe5 ♖xh1
30.♕e4++–) 29.e4+ ♔f4 30.♕f6#]

(1)

► **G. Kamsky**
► **I. Sokolov**
Rilton Cup Stockholm, 01.01.2017

1. +−

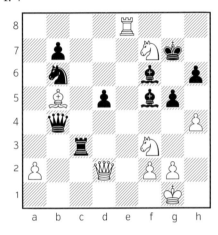

(2)

► **E. Blomqvist**
► **M. Kravtsiv**
Rilton Cup Stockholm, 02.01.2017

1.+−

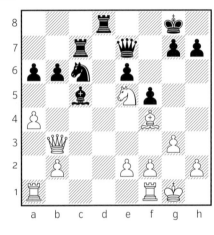

(3)

► **I. Sokolov**
► **S. Swapnil**
Rilton Cup Stockholm, 03.01.2017

1...−+

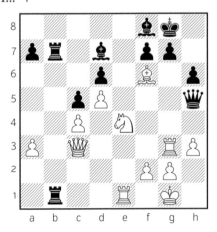

(4)

► **J. Haug**
► **J. Hammer**
Norwegian Champ. Blitz, 06.01.2017

1...−+

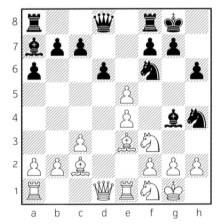

(5)

► **J. Hammer**
► **A. Neiksans**
Internet Pro League Rapid, 11.01.2017

1...−+

(6)

► **K. Kulaots**
► **G. Meier**
Swedish League, 14.01.2017

1.+−

(7)

► **P. Harikrishna**
► **B. Adhiban**
Wijk aan Zee, 15.01.2017

1.+−

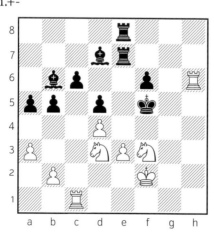

(8)

► **S. Karjakin**
► **L. Aronian**
Wijk aan Zee, 21.01.2017

1.+−

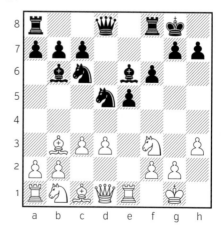

(9)

► **V. Topalov**
► **T. Paehtz**
Gibraltar Masters, 24.01.2017

1.+-

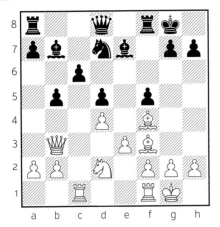

(10)

► **J. Bellon Lopez**
► **P. Svidler**
Gibraltar Masters, 24.01.2017

1...−+

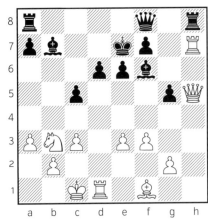

(11)

► **J. Carlstedt**
► **G. Oparin**
Gibraltar Masters, 27.01.2017

1.+-

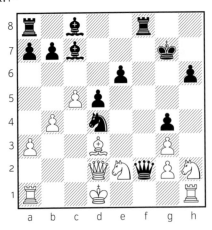

(12)

► **F. Peralta**
► **A. Delorme**
Catalan League, 28.01.2017

1.+-

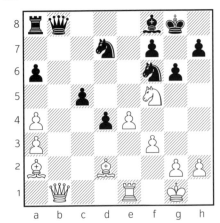

(13)

► **D. Shengelia**
► **K. Miton**
Czech League, 29.01.2017

1. +/-

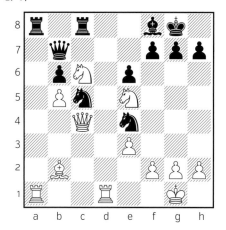

(14)

► **P. Michalik**
► **D. Sadzikowski**
Czech League, 29.01.2017

1.+-

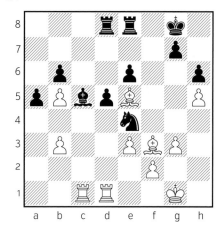

(15)

► **E. Hansen**
► **I. Smirin**
Wijk aan Zee, 29.01.2017

1.+-

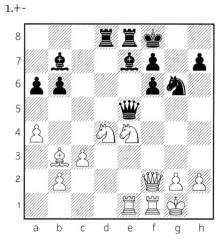

(16)

► **I. Ortiz Suarez**
► **K. Oliva Castaneda**
Cuban Championship, 10.02.2017

1.+-

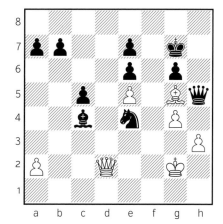

(17)

► **M. Khachiyan**
► **R. Svane**
Internet Pro League Rapid, 11.02.2017

1.=

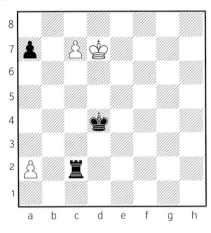

(18)

► **M. Bartel**
► **A. Szabo Gergely**
Hungarian League, 12.02.2017

1.+-

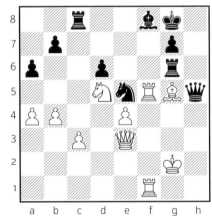

(19)

► **L. Dominguez Perez**
► **J. Van Foreest**
Internet Pro League Rapid, 15.02.2017

1...=

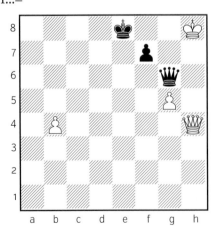

(20)

► **J. Van Foreest**
► **A. Neiksans**
Bundesliga, 18.02.2017

1...−+

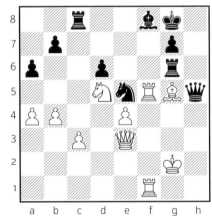

(21)

► **G. Papp**
► **E. Rozentalis**
Bundesliga 2, 18.02.2017

1.+-

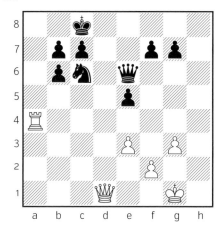

(22)

► **L. McShane**
► **S. Bromberger**
Bundesliga, 18.02.2017

1.+-

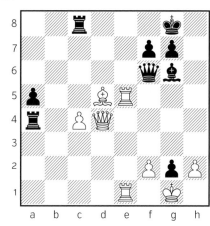

(23)

► **M. Adams**
► **S. Salem**
Sharjah Fide GP, 18.02.2017

1.+-

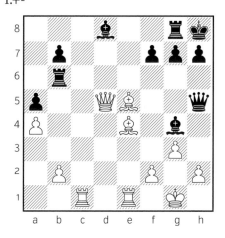

(24)

► **R. Van Kampen**
► **T. Gharamian**
Bundesliga, 19.02.2017

1...-/+

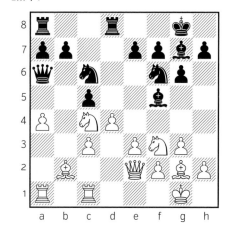

(25)

► **F. Levin**
► **B. Socko**
Bundesliga, 19.02.2017

1...–+

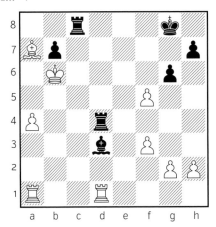

(26)

► **G. Gajewski**
► **K. Landa**
Bundesliga, 19.02.2017

1.+–

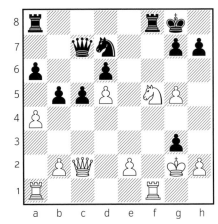

(27)

► **K. Sasikiran**
► **R. Svane**
Aeroflot Open Moscow, 22.02.2017

1.+–

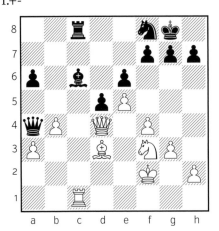

(28)

► **M. Tabatabaei**
► **J. Vakhidov**
Aeroflot Open Moscow, 25.02.2017

1.+–

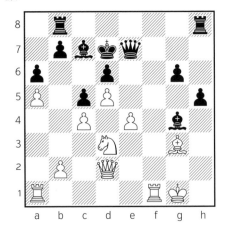

(29)

► A. Gorovets
► E. Moradiabadi

Burlingame Chinggis, 25.02.2017

1...–+

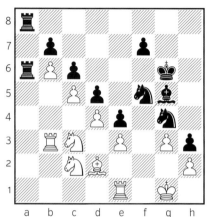

(30)

► E. Blomqvist
► M. Bluebaum

Aeroflot Open Moscow, 28.02.2017

1...–/+

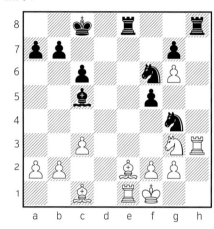

(31)

► N. Grandelius
► P. Nielsen

Swedish League, 04.03.2017

1.+–

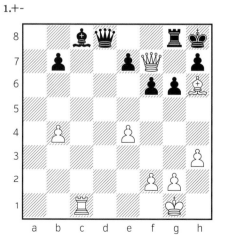

(32)

► T. Arnason
► A. Jakubiec

Icelandic League, 04.03.2017

1...–+

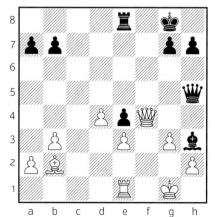

(33)

▶ **A. Pavlidis**
▶ **A. Kelires**
Greek Championship, 08.03.2017

1...−+

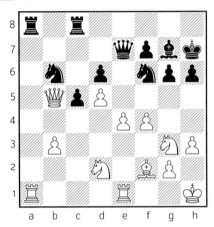

(34)

▶ **M. Khachiyan**
▶ **W. So**
Internet Pro League Rapid, 08.03.2017

1.+−

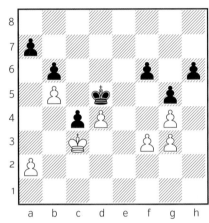

(35)

▶ **Q. Le**
▶ **T. Vo**
HD Bank Open, 12.03.2017

1.+−

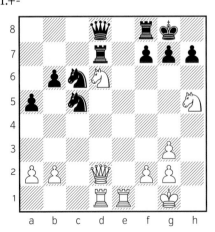

(36)

▶ **A. Baryshpolets**
▶ **I. Chirila**
Saint Louis Winter-B, 16.03.2017

1.+−

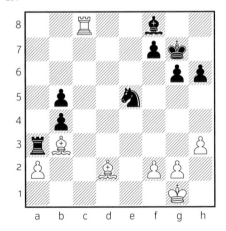

(37)

► T. Tran
► P. Michalik

HD Bank Open, 17.03.2017

1.+-

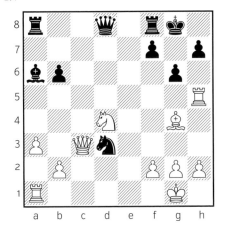

(38)

► I. Saric
► J. Smeets

Bundesliga, 18.03.2017

1.+-

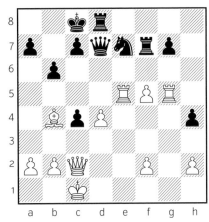

(39)

► V. Mikhalevski
► A. Bohus

Budapest Spring Open, 18.03.2017

1.+-

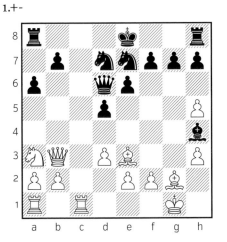

(40)

► R. Huebner
► M. Stojanovic

Swiss League, 19.03.2017

1.+-

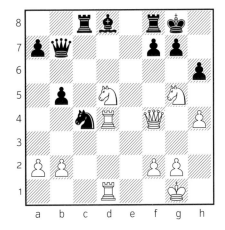

(41)

▶ E. Levin
▶ D. Fraiman
St. Petersburg, 24.03.2017

1...−+

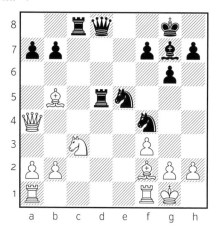

(42)

▶ F. Berkes
▶ G. Aczel
Budapest Spring Open, 24.03.2017

1. +/−

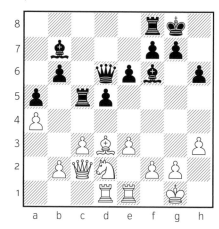

(43)

▶ B. Savchenko
▶ F. Berkes
Budapest Spring Open, 25.03.2017

1.+−

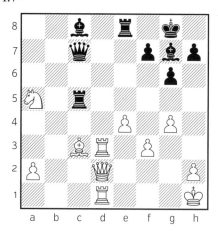

(44)

▶ G. Kamsky
▶ V. Akobian
USA Championship, 30.03.2017

1...−+

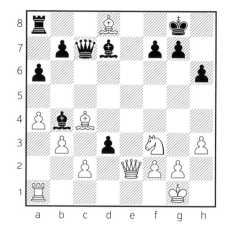

(45)

▶ M. Marin
▶ K. Lupulescu
Romanian Championship, 01.04.2017

1...−+

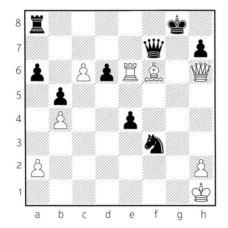

(46)

▶ C. Lupulescu
▶ V. Nevednichy
Romanian Championship, 02.04.2017

1.+−

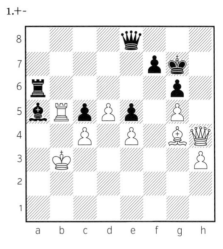

(47)

▶ H. Nakamura
▶ A. Onischuk
USA Championship, 07.04.2017

1... −/+

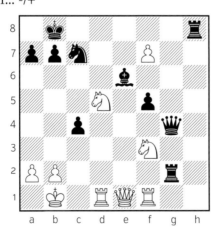

(48)

▶ S. Vidit
▶ M. Antipov
Dubai Open, 08.04.2017

1.+−

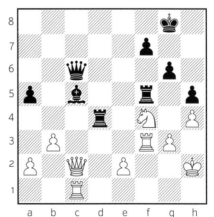

(49)

► E. Iturrizaga Bonelli
► L. Pantsulaia
Dubai Open, 08.04.2017

1.+-

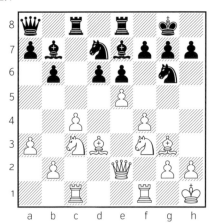

(50)

► K. Landa
► J. Van Foreest
Bundesliga, 09.04.2017

1.+-

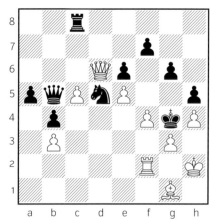

(51)

► A. Rakhmanov
► J. Santos Latasa
Dubai Open, 11.04.2017

1.+-

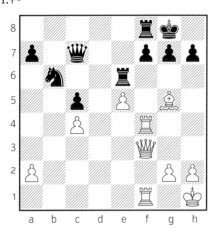

(52)

► A. Smirnov
► M. Krasenkow
Doeberl Cup Canberra, 14.04.2017

1...−+

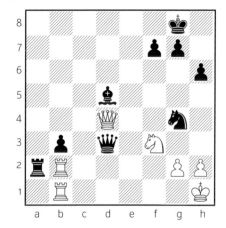

(53)

► **G. Antal**
► **E. Vorobiov**
La Roda Open, 15.04.2017

1...−+

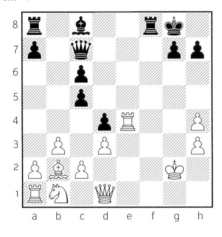

(54)

► **A. Seyb**
► **A. Graf**
Karlsruhe Grenke Open, 17.04.2017

1.+−

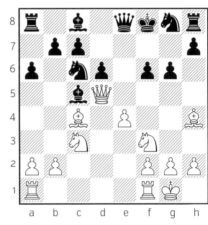

(55)

► **M. Vachier-Lagrave**
► **Y. Hou**
Grenke Chess Classic, 19.04.2017

1.+−

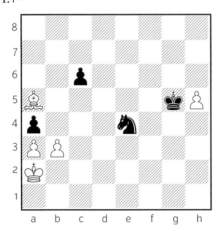

(56)

► **E. Rozentalis**
► **A. Brkic**
Austrian League, 21.04.2017

1.+−

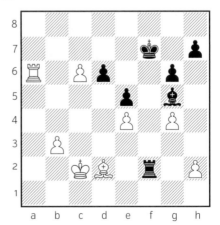

(57)

► **B. Firat**
► **M. Kleinman**
Reykjavik Open, 22.04.2017

1...−+

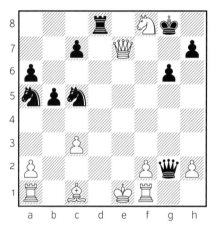

(58)

► **A. Denk**
► **J. Nunn**
World Champ. Seniors 50, 25.04.2017

1...−+

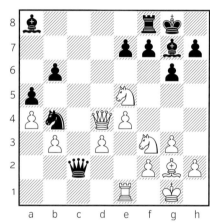

(59)

► **D. Flores**
► **H. Van Riemsdijk**
Szmetan Memorial, 26.04.2017

1.+−

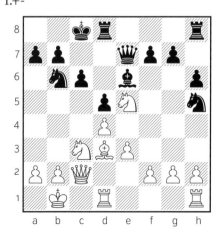

(60)

► **S. Movsesian**
► **M. Yilmaz**
Reykjavik Open, 27.04.2017

1.+−

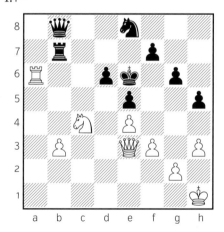

(61)

▶ **N. Altini**
▶ **S. Brunello**
Italian League, 30.04.2017

1...–+

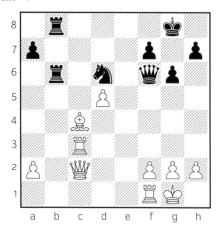

(62)

▶ **A. Grischuk**
▶ **B. Grachev**
Russian League, 05.05.2017

1.+-

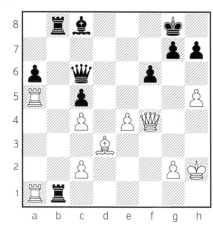

(63)

▶ **A. Grischuk**
▶ **K. Alekseenko**
Russian League, 08.05.2017

1.+-

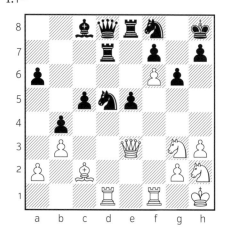

(64)

▶ **F. Vallejo Pons**
▶ **T. Radjabov**
Fide GP Moscow, 15.05.2017

1...–+

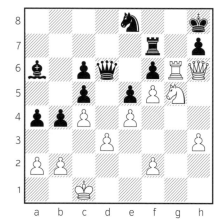

(65)

▶ **H. Stefansson**
▶ **G. Kjartansson**
Icelandic Championship, 15.05.2017

1... -/+

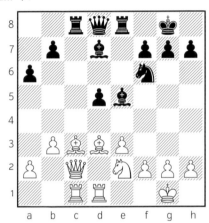

(66)

▶ **Y. Pelletier**
▶ **C. Vitoux**
French League, 19.05.2017

1...−+

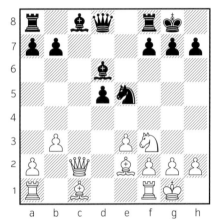

(67)

▶ **J. Xiong**
▶ **V. Akobian**
Saint Louis Spring-A, 20.05.2017

1...−+

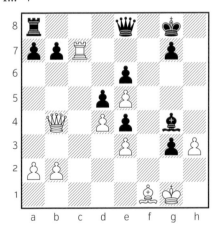

(68)

▶ **T. Sanikidze**
▶ **A. Sokolov**
French League, 20.05.2017

1. +/-

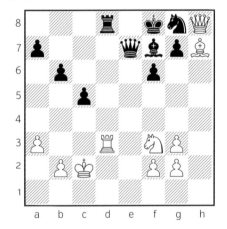

(69)

▶ **A. David**
▶ **M. Palac**
French League, 21.05.2017

1.+-

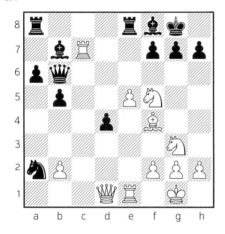

(70)

▶ **A. David**
▶ **M. Cornette**
French League, 25.05.2017

1...−+

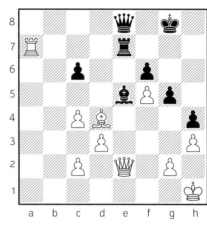

(71)

▶ **I. Nyzhnyk**
▶ **R. Li**
Chicago Open, 29.05.2017

1. +/-

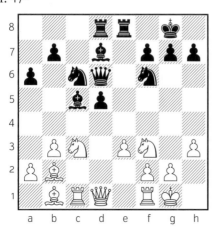

(72)

▶ **S. Das**
▶ **Z. Rahman**
Bhubaneswar Open, 29.05.2017

1... -/+

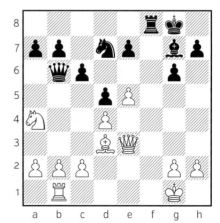

(73)

► **E. Sutovsky**
► **L. Paichadze**
European Championship, 02.06.2017

1...–+

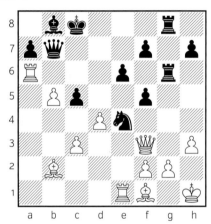

(74)

► **B. Dastan**
► **I. Saric**
European Championship, 03.06.2017

1...–+

(75)

► **V. Ivanchuk**
► **K. Piorun**
Capablanca Memorial, 04.06.2017

1...–+

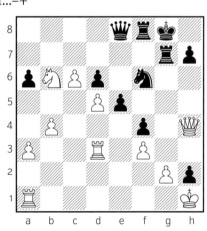

(76)

► **R. Ponomariov**
► **B. Macieja**
European Championship, 05.06.2017

1. +/–

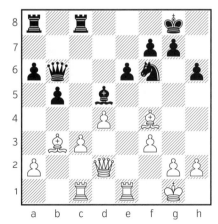

(77)

► **S. Shankland**
► **V. Ivanchuk**
Capablanca Memorial, 06.06.2017

1.+-

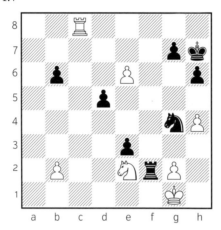

(78)

► **P. Ponkratov**
► **R. Ponomariov**
European Championship, 06.06.2017

1...-+

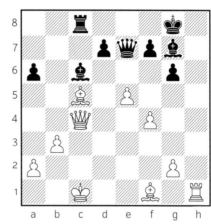

(79)

► **E. Sutovsky**
► **D. Forcen Esteban**
European Championship, 08.06.2017

1.+-

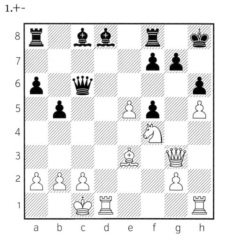

(80)

► **D. Khismatullin**
► **D. Sadzikowski**
European Championship, 09.06.2017

1. +/-

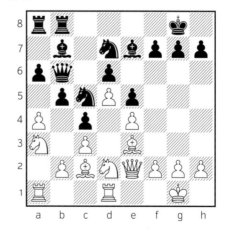

[81]

▶ A. Giri
▶ V. Anand
Norway Chess Stavanger, 10.06.2017

1.+-

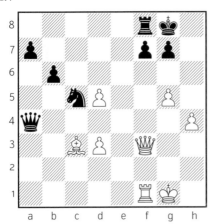

[82]

▶ G. Kaidanov
▶ E. Iturrizaga Bonelli
American Continental R, 18.06.2017

1... -/+

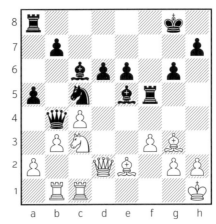

[83]

▶ F. Caruana
▶ E. Bacrot
Paris GCT Rapid, 22.06.2017

1...-+

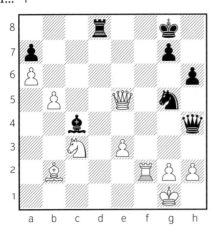

[84]

▶ A. Strikovic
▶ S. Del Rio de Angelis
Sanxenxo Carlos Open, 23.06.2017

1.+-

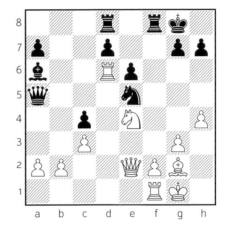

(85)

► E. Bacrot
► W. So
Paris GCT Blitz, 24.06.2017

1...=

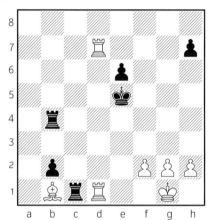

(86)

► S. Mamedyarov
► F. Caruana
Paris GCT Blitz, 25.06.2017

1...=

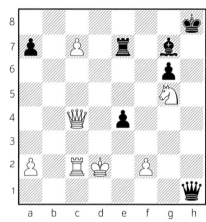

(87)

► F. Caruana
► A. Grischuk
Paris GCT Blitz, 25.06.2017

1...−+

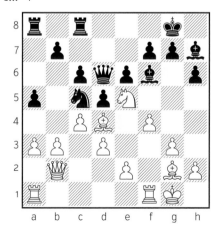

(88)

► L'Ami,E
► L. Van Wely
Dutch Championship, 27.06.2017

1.+-

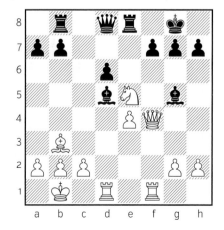

(89)

▶ B. Bok
▶ J. Van Foreest
Dutch Championship, 27.06.2017

1...−+

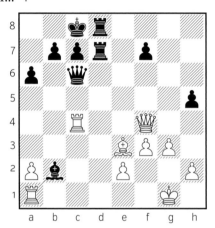

(90)

▶ S. Ernst
▶ T. Burg
Dutch Championship, 30.06.2017

1.+-

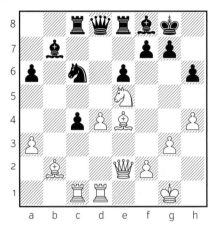

(91)

▶ F. Peralta
▶ L. Henderson de la Fuente
Montcada Open, 01.07.2017

1...−+

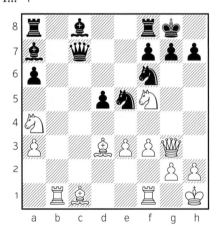

(92)

▶ L. Ljubojevic
▶ J. Timman
Platja d'Aro Legends Blitz, 01.07.2017

1...−+

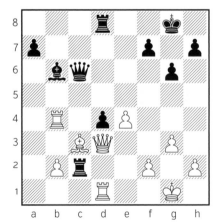

(93)

▶ S. Atalik
▶ O. Sahin
Nis Open, 04.07.2017

1.+-

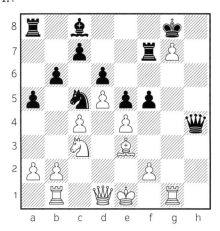

(94)

▶ L. Van Wely
▶ A. David
Greek League, 07.07.2017

1...=

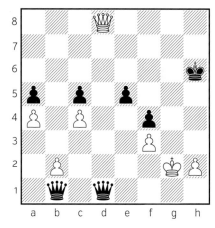

(95)

▶ T. Radjabov
▶ P. Eljanov
Fide GP Geneva, 07.07.2017

1.+-

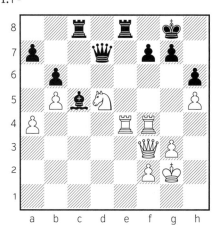

(96)

▶ I. Nepomniachtchi
▶ Y. Hou
Fide GP Geneva, 09.07.2017

1.+-

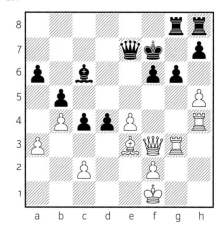

(97)

▶ **D. Debashis**
▶ **F. Sieber**
Najdorf Memorial Warsaw, 09.07.2017

1. +/-

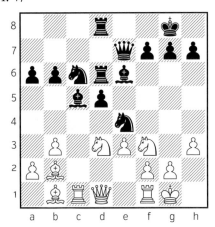

(98)

▶ **D. Bocharov**
▶ **V. Artemiev**
Russian Higher League, 09.07.2017

1...−+

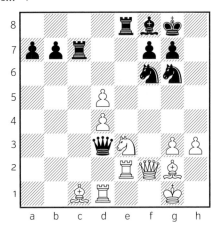

(99)

▶ **Y. Hou**
▶ **R. Rapport**
Fide GP Geneva, 10.07.2017

1...−+

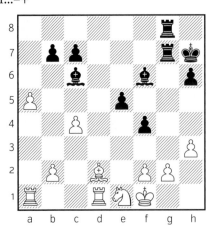

(100)

▶ **R. Ponomariov**
▶ **V. Malakhov**
Danzhou, 16.07.2017

1. +/-

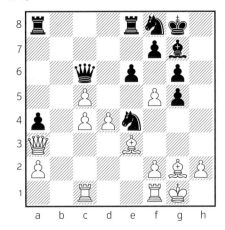

(101)

► H. Martirosyan
► H. Gabuzyan
Lake Sevan Martuni, 16.07.2017

1.+-

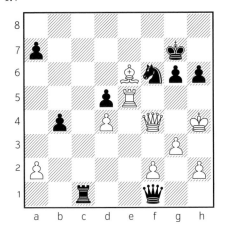

(102)

► A. Hauchard
► M. Demidov
Pardubice Rapid Open, 20.07.2017

1...−+

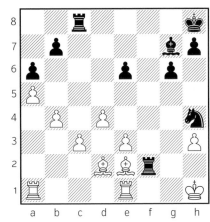

(103)

► D. Paravyan
► K. Bryzgalin
Pardubice Open, 23.07.2017

1.+-

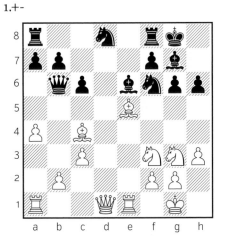

(104)

► F. Urkedal
► I. Sokolov
Helsingor Xtracon Open, 25.07.2017

1.+-

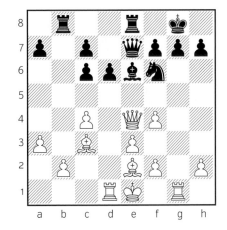

(105)

▶ **R. Yu**
▶ **A. Moiseenko**
Chinese League, 26.07.2017

1... -/+

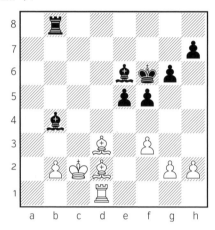

(106)

▶ **A. Brkic**
▶ **V. Bukal**
Pardubice Open, 26.07.2017

1.+-

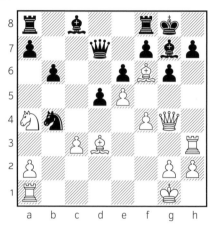

(107)

▶ **A. Liang**
▶ **R. Praggnanandhaa**
Millennials U14, 28.07.2017

1...−+

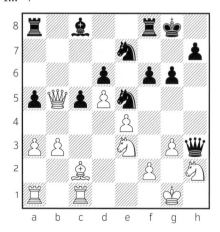

(108)

▶ **E. Safarli**
▶ **L. Pantsulaia**
Turkish League, 29.07.2017

1.+-

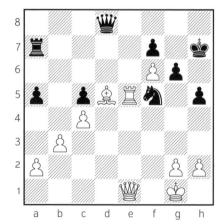

(109)

► **M. Vachier-Lagrave**
► **W. So**
Sinquefield Cup, 02.08.2017

1.+-

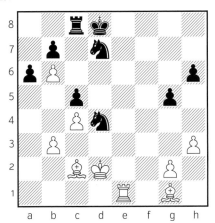

(110)

► **H. Tikkanen**
► **I. Saric**
Lund CellaVision Cup, 05.08.2017

1...−+

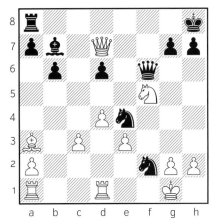

(111)

► **R. Svane**
► **G. Meier**
German Masters, 05.08.2017

1.+-

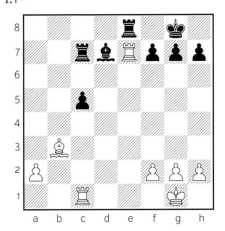

(112)

► **C. Sochacki**
► **A. Dgebuadze**
Charleroi Open, 05.08.2017

1... -/+

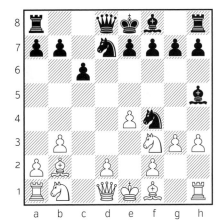

(113)

▶ M. Carlsen
▶ M. Vachier Lagrave

Sinquefield Cup, 05.08.2017

1...−+

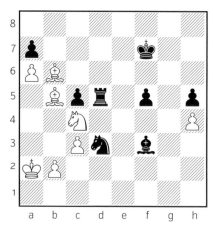

(114)

▶ E. Vorobiov
▶ I. Semjonovs

Riga Tech Open, 07.08.2017

1.+−

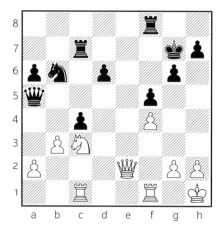

(115)

▶ L. Aronian
▶ W. So

Sinquefield Cup, 08.08.2017

1.+−

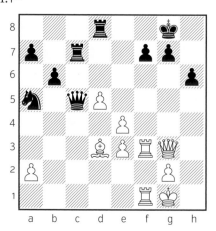

(116)

▶ M. Ulybin
▶ A. Czajkowski

Warakomska Memorial, 11.08.2017

1.+−

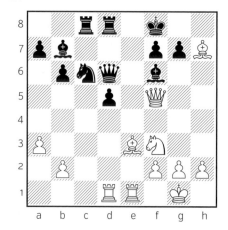

(117)

► **R. Ponomariov**
► **D. Forcen Esteban**
Spanish Champ. Rapid, 13.08.2017

1.+-

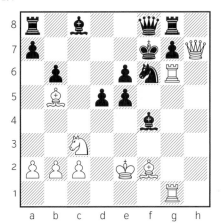

(118)

► **L. Perez Rodriguez**
► **B. Sambuev**
Quebec Open, 13.08.2017

1...−+

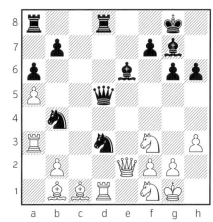

(119)

► **T. Laurusas**
► **V. Kunin**
Riga Tech Open, 13.08.2017

1.+-

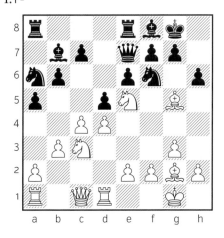

(120)

► **E. Iturrizaga Bonelli**
► **R. Ponomariov**
Spanish League, 14.08.2017

1... -/+

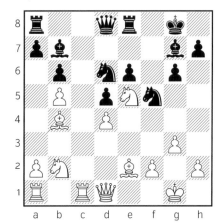

(121)

▶ L. Aronian
▶ D. Navara

Saint Louis Rapid, 14.08.2017

1.+-

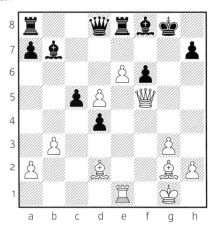

(122)

▶ A. Areshchenko
▶ T. Banusz

Spanish League, 14.08.2017

1.+-

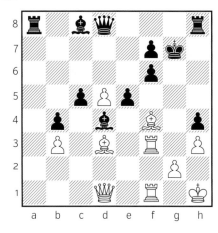

(123)

▶ L. Martinez Duany
▶ J. Santos Latasa

Spanish League, 15.08.2017

1.+-

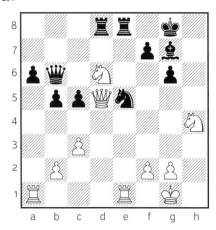

(124)

▶ O. Barbosa
▶ E. Perelshteyn

Washington Open, 15.08.2017

1.+-

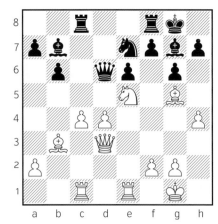

(125)

► **A. Demchenko**
► **S. Movsesian**
Spanish League, 19.08.2017

1.+-

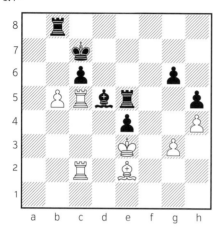

(126)

► **S. Vidit**
► **A. Areshchenko**
Spanish League, 20.08.2017

1.+-

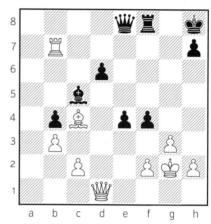

(127)

► **A. Fawzy**
► **P. Maghsoodloo**
Abu Dhabi Open, 21.08.2017

1. +/-

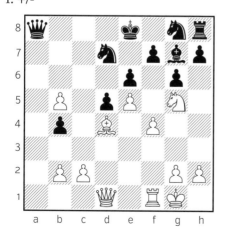

(128)

► **B. Amin**
► **S. Salem**
Abu Dhabi Open, 21.08.2017

1.+-

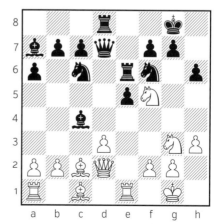

(129)

▶ F. Berkes
▶ P. Schlosser

Schwarzach Open, 26.08.2017

1.+-

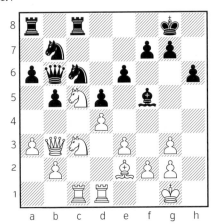

(130)

▶ G. Kamsky
▶ A. Sarana

St. Petersburg Rapid, 27.08.2017

1.+-

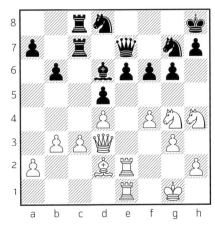

(131)

▶ A. Demuth
▶ P. Duboue

French Champ. Accession, 27.08.2017

1.+-

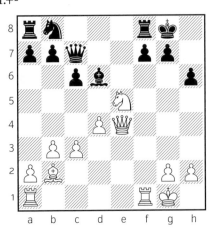

(132)

▶ H. Wang
▶ D. Sengupta

Fide World Cup Tbilisi, 04.09.2017

1.+-

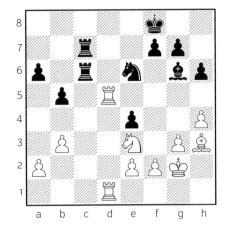

(133)

▶ **V. Plat**
▶ **P. Stoma**
Polish League, 04.09.2017

1.+-

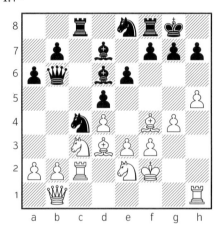

(134)

▶ **I. Ivanisevic**
▶ **V. Sanal**
Serbian League, 06.09.2017

1.+-

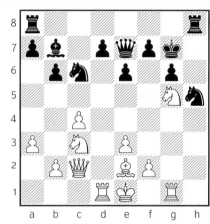

(135)

▶ **A. Motylev**
▶ **A. Giri**
Fide World Cup Tbilisi, 08.09.2017

1... -/+

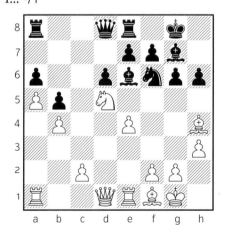

(136)

▶ **V. Ivanchuk**
▶ **J. Duda**
Fide World Cup Tbilisi, 08.09.2017

1. +/-

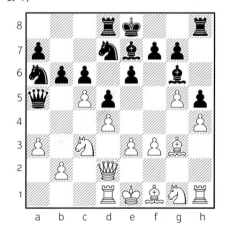

(137)

▶ D. Bocharov
▶ S. Khanin
Kurnosov Memorial Rapid, 10.09.2017

1...−+

(138)

▶ M. Matlakov
▶ L. Aronian
Fide World Cup Tbilisi, 11.09.2017

1.+-

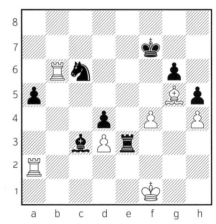

(139)

▶ L. Ding
▶ S. Vidit
Fide World Cup Tbilisi, 11.09.2017

1.+-

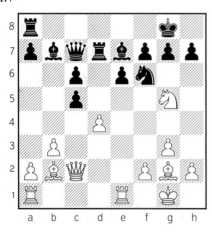

(140)

▶ R. Rapport
▶ E. Najer
Fide World Cup Tbilisi, 14.09.2017

1...=

(141)

▶ **M. Parligras**
▶ **K. Georgiev**
Serbian League, 18.09.2017

1.+-

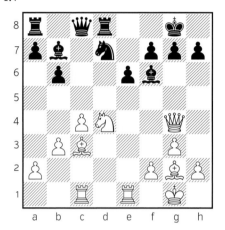

(142)

▶ **L. Aronian**
▶ **M. Vachier Lagrave**
Fide World Cup Tbilisi, 21.09.2017

1...=

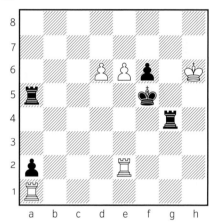

(143)

▶ **H. Gretarsson**
▶ **J. Ragnarsson**
Reykjavik Taflfelag Open, 22.09.2017

1.+-

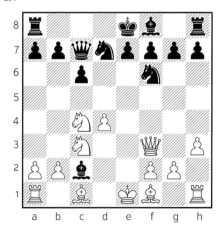

(144)

▶ **M. Carlsen**
▶ **J. Granda Zuniga**
Douglas IoM Open, 27.09.2017

1. +/-

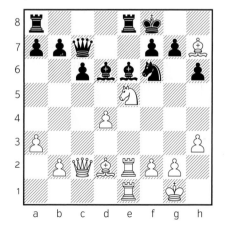

(145)

► F. Caruana
► G. Jones
Douglas IoM Open, 29.09.2017

1. +/-

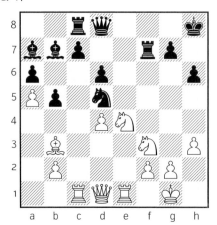

(146)

► R. Wojtaszek
► J. Tomczak
Polish League, 01.10.2017

1.+-

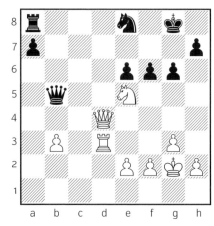

(147)

► W. Spoelman
► R. Edouard
Belgian League, 01.10.2017

1... -/+

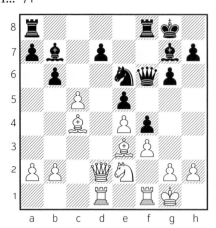

(148)

► V. Malakhov
► V. Fedoseev
European Club Cup, 10.10.2017

1.+-

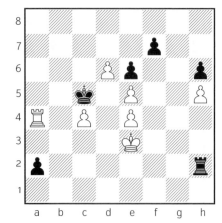

(149)

► **M. Ulybin**
► **G. Quparadze**
Stavanger Open, 11.10.2017

1...−+

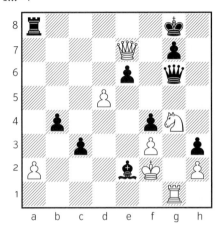

(150)

► **L. Krysa**
► **P. Acosta**
Argentinian Championship, 15.10.2017

1.+-

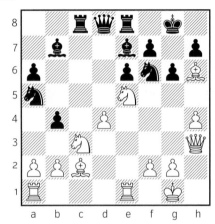

(151)

► **J. Bergthorsson**
► **J. Hjartarson**
Islandic League, 19.10.2017

1...−+

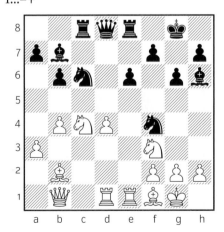

(152)

► **B. Jobava**
► **J. Hammer**
Swedish League, 20.10.2017

1...=

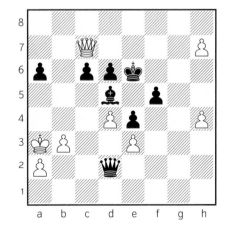

(153)

► **A. Goganov**
► **B. Jobava**
Swedish League, 21.10.2017

1...–+

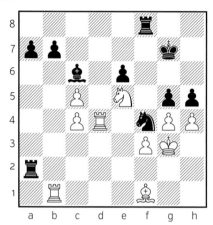

(154)

► **E. Cuberli**
► **D. Flores**
Argentine Championship, 22.10.2017

1...–+

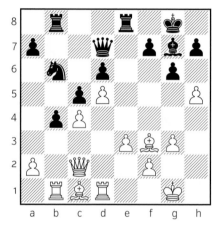

(155)

► **F. Rambaldi**
► **L. Bruzon Batista**
Spice Cup Open, 25.10.2017

1...–+

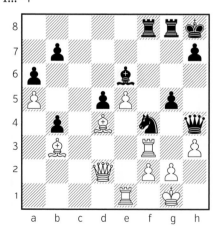

(156)

► **S. Golubov**
► **S. Sjugirov**
Chigorin Memorial, 25.10.2017

1... -/+

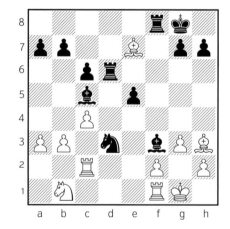

(157)

► V. Erdos
► H. Steingrimsson
European Team Cham., 28.10.2017

1.+-

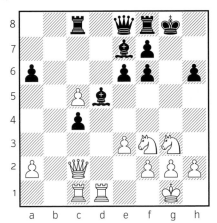

(158)

► A. Rasmussen
► T. Nyback
European Team Champ., 30.10.2017

1.+-

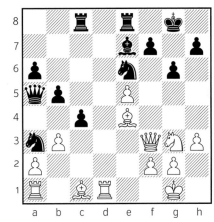

(159)

► V. Kovalev
► D. Pavasovic
European Team Champ., 30.10.2017

1.+-

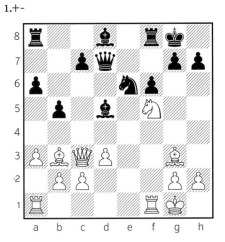

(160)

► A. Naiditsch
► N. Morozov
European Team Champ., 31.10.2017

1.+-

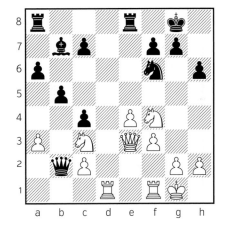

(161)

► **M. Bluebaum**
► **M. Bosiocic**
European Team Champ., 01.11.2017

1...–+

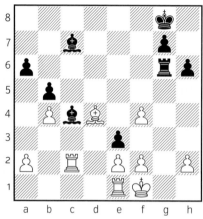

(162)

► **G. Antal**
► **A. Adly**
Tegernsee Open, 01.11.2017

1...–+

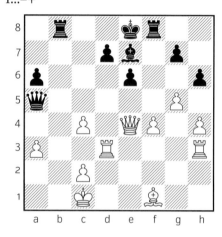

(163)

► **D. Howell**
► **J. Lopez Martinez**
European Team Champ., 04.11.2017

1.+-

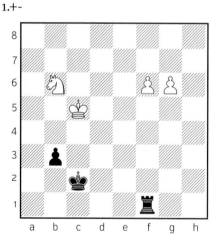

(164)

► **D. Vocaturo**
► **Y. Pelletier**
European Team Champ., 06.11.2017

1.+-

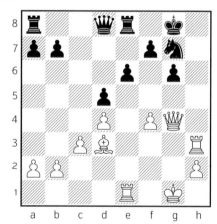

(165)

► F. Caruana
► A. Grischuk
Champions Showdown, 11.11.2017

1.+-

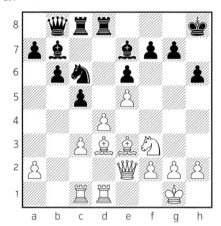

(166)

► B. Bogosavljevic
► N. Ostojic
Manojlovica Memoria, 17.11.2017

1.+-

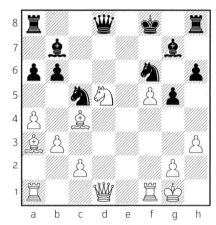

(167)

► R. Li
► R. Prasanna
UT Dallas Fall Open, 18.11.2017

1.+-

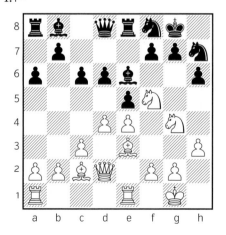

(168)

► G. Quparadze
► D. Paravyan
Gaprindashvili Cup Tbilisi, 19.11.2017

1.+-

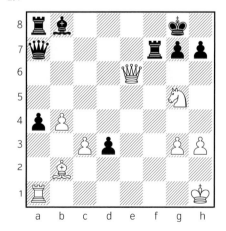

(169)

► T. Luther
► G. Papp
Austrian League, 19.11.2017

1...−+

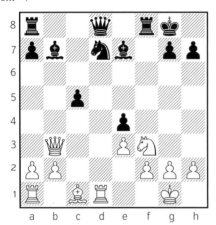

(170)

► V. Belous
► A. Baryshpolets
American Open Costa, 25.11.2017

1.+-

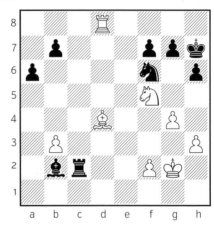

(171)

► A. Horvath
► L. Gyorkos
Hungarian League, 26.11.2017

1. +/-

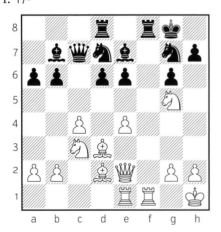

(172)

► P. Acs
► J. Konnyu
Hungarian League, 26.11.2017

1. +/-

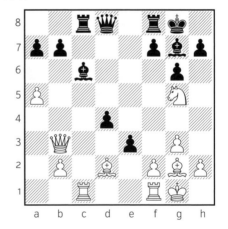

(173)

▶ Y. Shvayger
▶ E. Atalik

Holuj-Radzikowska, 30.11.2017

1.+-

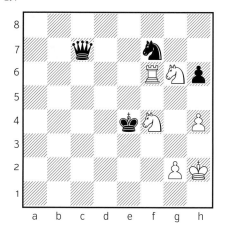

(174)

▶ M. Matlakov
▶ E. Inarkiev

Russian Championship, 05.12.2017

1.+-

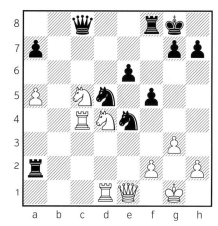

(175)

▶ L. Van Wely
▶ R. Kempinski

Bundesliga, 09.12.2017

1. +/-

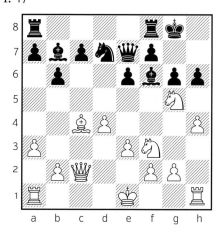

(176)

▶ S. Volkov
▶ N. Vitiugov

Russian Championship, 14.12.2017

1...−+

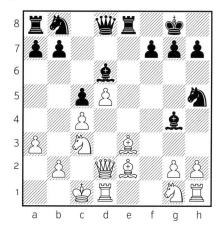

(177)

▶ **S. Lomasov**
▶ **N. Yakubboev**
World Youth U16, 14.12.2017

1.+-

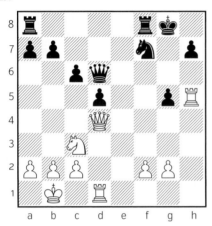

(178)

▶ **M. Kusiak**
▶ **M. Chigaev**
European Champ. Rapid, 16.12.2017

1...-+

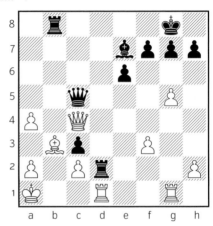

– SOLUTIONS –

(1)

▷ G. Kamsky
► I. Sokolov
Rilton Cup Stockholm, 01.01.2017

34.♘xh6! ♚xh6 [34...♕xb5 35.♘xf5+
♚g6 (35...♚h7 36.♘xg5+ ♚g6 37.g4+-)
36.♘e5+ ♚xf5 37.g4+ ♚e4 38.f3+ ♚xf3
39.♘c6++-] 35.hxg5+ ♚h7 36.gxf6
1-0

(2)

▷ E. Blomqvist
► M. Kravtsiv
Rilton Cup Stockholm, 02.01.2017

20.♘f3! ♖cd7 21.♗g5 ♕e8 22.♗xd8
♖xd8 23.♖fd1 ♖c8 24.e3 ♘a5 25.♕d3
1-0

(3)

▷ I. Sokolov
► S. Swapnil
Rilton Cup Stockholm, 03.01.2017

29...♕e2!! 30.♖xb1 ♖xb1+ 31.♔h2
♕d1 32.♖xg7+ ♗xg7 33.♗xg7
♕h1+ 34.♔g3 ♗xh3! 35.♗xh6 [35.
gxh3 ♕xe4-+] 35...♕xg2+ 36.♔f4 f5
37.♘f6+ ♚f7 38.♕e3 ♕h2+ 39.♔f3
♕g2+ 40.♔e2 ♖b2+ 0-1

(4)

▷ J. Haug
► J. Hammer
Norwegian Championship Blitz
Sandefjord, 06.01.2017

14...♗xf3! 15.gxf3 ♕c8 16.♗xa7
♕h3 17.♘e3 dxe5 18.♗c5 ♖fd8 0-1
[18...♖fd8 19.♕e2 ♘xf3+-+]

(5)

▷ J. Hammer
► A. Neiksans
Internet Pro League Rapid,
11.01.2017

35...d3+! 36.♔d1 ♖b1+ 37.♔d2 ♖b2+
38.♔e1 [38.♔d1 ♘c3+ 39.♔e1 d2+-+;
38.♔e3 ♖e2#] 38...d2+ 39.♔e2 ♘c3+
40.♔e3 ♘d1+ 41.♔e2 ♘c3+ 42.♔e3
d1♕??= [42...d1N#!]

(6)

▷ K. Kulaots
► G. Meier
Swedish League, 14.01.2017

15.♗xf6! ♗xf6 16.♘xe6! fxe6
17.♕xe6+ ♔h8 18.♕f5 g6 19.♕xg6
♕c7 20.♕xh6+ ♔g8 21.♕g6+ ♔h8
[21...♔g7 22.♗c4+ ♔h8 23.♕h5+
♕h7 24.♕xh7+ ♔xh7 25.♖d7++-]
22.♗f5 [22.♖h3+-] 22...♗c8
23.♕h5+ ♔g8 24.♖d7!! 1-0 [24.♖d7
♕xd7 25.♗xd7 ♗xd7 26.♕d5++-]

(7)

▷ P. Harikrishna
► B. Adhiban
Wijk aan Zee, 15.01.2017

40.♘h4+! ♔g5 [40...♔e4 41.♖c3! ♖f7 42.♖h5 ♗g4 43.♔f1!! ♔xe3 (43...♗xh5 44.♘f2#) 44.♘f2+ ♔d2 45.♘xg4+-; 40...♔e6 41.♘f4+ ♔d6 42.♖xf6+ ♔c7 43.♘xd5++-] **41.♖g6+ ♔xh4 42.♖h1+ ♗h3 43.♖g3** 1–0

(8)

▷ S. Karjakin
► L. Aronian
Wijk aan Zee, 21.01.2017

11.d4?? [11.c4! ♘db4 12.c5+-] **11...♗f7 12.dxe5 ♘xe5 13.♗xd5 ♗xd5 14.♘xe5 fxe5 15.♗e3=**

(9)

▷ V. Topalov
► T. Paehtz
Gibraltar Masters, 24.01.2017

15.♗xd5+! cxd5 16.♖c7 1–0 [16.♖c7 ♖b8 17.♖xb7 ♖xb7 18.♕xd5++-]

(10)

▷ J. Bellon Lopez
► P. Svidler
Gibraltar Masters, 24.01.2017

21...♕g7! 22.♕h2 [22.♖xh8 ♖xh8 23.♕g4 ♗xc3-+; 22.♖xg7 ♖xh5-+] **22...♗d5 23.♖h3 ♗xc3 24.♘d4 cxd4 25.bxc3 dxe3 26.♖d4 ♖hc8** 0–1

(11)

▷ J. Carlstedt
► G. Oparin
Gibraltar Masters, 27.01.2017

22.♘f3! [22.♘xg4? ♕f1+-+] **22...♖f6** [22...gxf3 23.♕xh6+ ♔f7 24.♕g6+ ♔e7 25.♖h7+ ♔d8 26.♕g5++-] **23.♘fxd4 ♗e5 24.♔c2 ♗xd4 25.♖af1 ♕e3 26.♘xd4 ♕xd4 27.♖xh6! ♖xf1** [27...♖xh6 28.♕g5++-] **28.♕g5+** 1–0

(12)

▷ F. Peralta
► A. Delorme
Catalan League, 28.01.2017

25.♗xf7+! ♔xf7 [25...♔h8 26.♕xb8 ♖xb8 27.e5 gxf5 28.exf6 ♘xf6 29.♗c4+-] **26.♕a2+ ♔e8 27.♕e6+ ♔d8 28.♗a5+** 1–0

(13)

▷ D. Shengelia
► K. Miton
Czech League, 29.01.2017

25.♖xa8! ♖xa8 [25...♕xa8 26.♖a1 ♕b7 27.♖a7+-] **26.♘d8 ♕a7 27.♘exf7** [27.♘dxf7±] **27...♕a2 28.♕d4 h5 29.♖a1 ♕xa1+?** [29...♕b3!! 30.♖xa8 ♕c2 31.♖a1 ♘b3 32.♕e5 ♘xa1 33.h3 ♕xf2+ 34.♔h2 ♘d2=] **30.♗xa1 ♖a2 31.f3 ♘f6 32.♕d1 ♘d5 33.♕e1** 1–0

(14)

▷ P. Michalik
► D. Sadzikowski
Czech League, 29.01.2017

**34.♗xe4! dxe4 35.♖xd8 ♖xd8
36.♖xc5! bxc5 37.b6 c4** [37...♖d7
38.♗c7+-] **38.bxc4 ♖d1+ 39.♔g2
♖b1 40.c5 ♔f7 41.♗c7!** 1–0 [41.♗c7
a4 42.c6 a3 43.b7 a2 44.♗e5+-]

[15]

▷ **E. Hansen**
▶ **I. Smirin**
Wijk aan Zee, 29.01.2017

25.♘xf6! ♕xf6 26.♕g3! 1–0 [26.♕g3
♕g7 27.♘e6++-]

[16]

▷ **I. Ortiz Suarez**
▶ **K. Oliva Castaneda**
Cuban Championship Villa Clara,
10.02.2017

30.♗f6+! exf6 [30...♔f7 31.♕d8!
♘xf6 (31...♗f1+ 32.♔g1+-) 32.gxh5+-]
**31.♕d7+ ♔h6 32.gxh5 ♗d5 33.hxg6
♔xg6** +-

[17]

▷ **M. Khachiyan**
▶ **R. Svane**
Internet Pro League Rapid,
11.02.2017

62.a4?? [62.c8♕! ♖xc8 63.♔xc8
a5 64.♔d7! (64.♔c7? a4 65.♔b6 a3
66.♔b5 ♔c3 67.♔a4 ♔b2-+) 64...a4
65.♔e6! a3 66.♔f5! ♔c3 67.♔e4 ♔b2
68.♔d3 ♔xa2 69.♔c2=] **62...a5** 0–1
[62...a5 63.c8♕ ♖xc8 64.♔xc8 ♔c5

65.♔b7 ♔b4 66.♔c6 ♔xa4 67.♔c5
♔b3–+]

[18]

▷ **M. Bartel**
▶ **A. Szabo Gergely**
Hungarian League, 12.02.2017

19.♕xd5!! exd5 [19...♕xd5 20.♖xd5
exd5 21.♘f6+ gxf6 22.exf6+ ♗e7
23.♖xe7+ ♔f8 24.♖e5+ ♔g8
25.♖g5#] **20.♘f6+ gxf6 21.exf6+
♗e7 22.♖xe7+ ♔f8 23.♖e8+** 1–0 [23.
♖e8+ ♔xe8 24.♖e1#]

[19]

▷ **L. Dominguez Perez**
▶ **J. Van Foreest**
Internet Pro League Rapid,
15.02.2017

64...♕f5? [64...f6!! 65.gxf6?? (65.
b5 fxg5=) 65...♔f8 66.♕h7 ♕xf6+
67.♕g7+ ♕xg7#; 64...f5 65.b5+-]
**65.♕h6 ♕e5+ 66.♕f6 ♕e4 67.♔g8
♕xb4 68.♕xf7+** 1–0

[20]

▷ **J. Van Foreest**
▶ **A. Neiksans**
Bundesliga, 18.02.2017

35...♕g4+?? [35...♘f7! 36.♖xf7
♖xg5+ 37.♔f2 ♕xf7+-+] **36.♔h2
♘f7 37.♖g1?** [37.♖1f4! ♕d1 (37...
♕h5+ 38.♖h4 ♕d1 39.♖xf7 ♔xf7
40.♕f2+ ♔g8 41.♕a2+-) 38.♖xf7
♖xg5 39.♖xf8+ ♖xf8 40.♖xf8+ ♔xf8

41.♕xg5+-] 37...♘h6? 38.♖f4 ♕e6
39.♖g3 ♔h7 40.♕f3+-

(21)

▷ G. Papp
► E. Rozentalis
Bundesliga 2, 18.02.2017

28.♖a8+! ♘b8 29.♕h5! ♕e8
30.♕h3+! 1–0

(22)

▷ L. McShane
► S. Bromberger
Bundesliga, 18.02.2017

33.♕g4! ♖f8 34.♖e8 ♗f5 35.♕h5
♗e6 36.R1xe6! 1–0

(23)

▷ M. Adams
► S. Salem
Sharjah Fide GP, 18.02.2017

30.♖c5!? [30.♖c8! ♖h6 (30...♗e7
31.♖xg8+ ♔xg8 32.♕xa5 ♖h6 33.♕a8+
♗f8 34.h4+-; 30...♗xc8 31.♗xg7+ ♖xg7
32.♕xh5+-) 31.♖xd8 ♕xh2+ 32.♔f1
♗h3+ 33.♔e2+-] 30...♖h6 [30...♖e6
31.♕d4 ♕g5 32.h4 ♕e7 33.♖b5±]
31.h4 b6 32.♖b5 ♖e6? [32...♗e2!?
33.♗d3 ♖xd3 34.♕xd3 ♕g6 35.♕xg6
♖xg6 36.♖d1±] 33.♕d4! f6 34.♗xf6
♗xf6 35.♕xh5 ♗xh5 [35...♗xd4??
36.♖xh7#] 36.♕c4 +-

(24)

▷ R. Van Kampen
► T. Gharamian
Bundesliga, 19.02.2017

14...♘a5! 15.♘fd2 ♗e6 16.♗f1 ♗xc4
17.♘xc4 ♘b3 18.♕f3 ♘xa1 19.♖xa1
cxd4 20.cxd4 ♖ac8∓

(25)

▷ F. Levin
► B. Socko
Bundesliga, 19.02.2017

32...♖b4+! [32...♖d6+ 33.♔a5 ♖a6+
34.♔b4 ♗c2 35.♗c5 ♗xd1 36.♖xd1∓]
33.♔a5 ♖b2! 0–1 [33...♖b2 34.♖xd3
♖a8–+]

(26)

▷ G. Gajewski
► K. Landa
Bundesliga, 19.02.2017

24.♘e7+! ♔h8 25.hxg3 g6 [25...♘e5
26.♕xh7+! ♔xh7 27.♖h1#] 26.♖xf8+
♖xf8 [26...♘xf8 27.♕c3#] 27.♘xg6+
1–0

(27)

▷ K. Sasikiran
► R. Svane
Aeroflot Open Moscow, 22.02.2017

23.b5! axb5 24.♕xa4 bxa4 25.♗a6
♗b7 [25...♖c7 26.♘d4+-] 26.♖xc8
♗xa6 27.♖b8 1–0

[28]

▷ M. Tabatabaei
► J. Vakhidov
Aeroflot Open Moscow, 25.02.2017

29.♘xc5+! dxc5 30.d6 ♗xd6 31.♖f7!
1–0 [31.♖f7 ♕xf7 32.♕xd6+ ♔e8
33.♕xb8++-]

[29]

▷ A. Gorovets
► E. Moradiabadi
Burlingame Chinggis, 25.02.2017

35...♖a2! 36.♘xa2 [36.♖c1 ♘xd4–
+] **36...♖xa2 37.♖c3 ♘xd4 38.♘xd4**
[38.exd4 ♗xd2–+] **38...♖xd2 39.♖c2**
♗xe3+ 40.♔h1 [40.♖xe3 ♖d1+
41.♖e1 ♖xe1#] **40...♖xd4 41.♖xe3**
♖d1+ 0–1

[30]

▷ E. Blomqvist
► M. Bluebaum
Aeroflot Open Moscow, 28.02.2017

21...♘h2+! 22.♖xh2 [22.♔g1 ♖xh3
23.gxh3 ♘f3+ 24.♔f1 ♘xe1∓] **22...**
♖xh2 23.♗f3 ♘e4 24.♗xe4 fxe4
25.♖xe4 ♖xe4 26.♘xe4 ♖h1+
27.♔e2 ♗xf2∓

[31]

▷ N. Grandelius
► P. Nielsen
Swedish League, 04.03.2017

28.e5! fxe5 [28...♕e8 29.♗g7+!+-]
29.♖xc8! ♕xc8 30.♕xe7 ♕f5 31.g4
1–0

[32]

▷ T. Arnason
► A. Jakubiec
Icelandic League, 04.03.2017

29...♖f8! 30.g4 [30.♕xe4 ♕e2!
31.♕e6+ ♔h8!!–+] **30...♕b5** 0–1 [30...
♕b5 31.♕g3 ♕f1+ 32.♖xf1 ♖xf1#]

[33]

▷ A. Pavlidis
► A. Kelires
Greek Championship Thessaloniki,
08.03.2017

31...♘g4! 32.hxg4 [32.♖xa8 ♘xf2+
33.♔g1 ♖xa8 34.♔xf2 ♗d4+ 35.♔f1
♕h4–+] **32...♗xa1 33.♕xb6 ♗c3!**
34.♘gf1 ♖cb8 35.♕c6 ♕d8! 36.♘c4
♗xe1 37.♗xe1 ♖a1 38.♗g3 ♖xf1+
39.♔h2 ♖xb3 40.e5 ♖bb1 0–1

[34]

▷ M. Khachiyan
► W. So
Internet Pro League Rapid,
08.03.2017

38.a3?? [38.f4! gxf4 39.gxf4 ♔e4 (39...
f5 40.g5! *(40.gxf5? h5 41.f6 ♔e6–+)*
40...hxg5 41.fxg5 f4 42.g6 ♔e6 43.d5+
♔f6 44.d6+-) 40.f5! ♔f4 41.d5! ♔e5
42.♔xc4 ♔d6 43.♔d4 ♔d7 44.d6!
♔xd6 45.a3! ♔c7 46.♔d5 ♔d7

47.a4+-] **38...f5! 39.gxf5** [39.a4 f4 40.gxf4 gxf4-+] **39...h5 40.f6 ♔e6** 0–1

(35)

▷ Q. Le
▶ T. Vo
Ho Chi Minh City ʜᴅ Bank Open, 12.03.2017

25.♕c3! f6 [25...♕g5 26.♖d5! ♕g6 27.♘f4+-] **26.♕c4+ ♔h8 27.♘f7+! ♖fxf7 28.♕xf7 ♖xf7 29.♖xd8+** 1–0

(36)

▷ A. Baryshpolets
▶ I. Chirila
Saint Louis Winter-B, 16.03.2017

30.♖xf8! ♖xb3 [30...♔xf8 31.♗xb4++-] **31.♗xh6+ ♔xh6 32.axb3** 1–0

(37)

▷ T. Tran
▶ P. Michalik
Ho Chi Minh City ʜᴅ Bank Open, 17.03.2017

26.♘e6! fxe6 27.♗xe6+ ♖f7 28.♗xf7+ ♔xf7 29.♖xh7+ ♔e6 30.♕c6+ ♔e5 31.♖d7 1–0

(38)

▷ I. Saric
▶ J. Smeets
Bundesliga, 18.03.2017

28.♗xe7! ♖xe7 29.♕e4! 1–0 [29.♕e4 ♖xe5 30.♕a8#]

(39)

▷ V. Mikhalevski
▶ A. Bohus
Budapest Spring Open, 18.03.2017

18.♕a4! [18.♕xb7 ♖b8 19.♕c7 ♕xc7 20.♖xc7±] **18...♗f6 19.♘b5 axb5** [19...♕b8 20.♘c7++-] **20.♕xa8+ ♕b8 21.♕xb8+ ♘xb8 22.♖c7 ♗xb2 23.♖b1** 1–0

(40)

▷ R. Huebner
▶ M. Stojanovic
Swiss League, 19.03.2017

27.♕e4! hxg5 28.♘f6+ ♗xf6 29.♕xb7 gxh4 30.♕xb5 ♗xd4 31.♖xd4 ♘b6 32.♖xh4 +-

(41)

▷ E. Levin
▶ D. Fraiman
St. Petersburg, 24.03.2017

21...♘xf3+! 22.gxf3 ♕g5+ 23.♗g3 ♗d4+! **24.♖f2** [24.♔h1 ♕xg3! 25.hxg3 ♖h5#] **24...♘h3+ 25.♔g2 ♖xc3! 26.bxc3 ♗xf2 27.♗e2 ♗xg3 28.hxg3 ♕e3 29.♕e4 ♕f2+** 0–1

(42)

▷ F. Berkes
► G. Aczel
Budapest Spring Open, 24.03.2017

21.♗h7+! ♔h8 22.♘e4 ♕e5 23.♘xc5 bxc5 24.♗d3 c4 25.♗e2 ♗d8 26.♗f3±

(43)

▷ B. Savchenko
► F. Berkes
Budapest Spring Open, 25.03.2017

39.♖d8! ♗xc3 [39...♖f8 40.♗b4 ♖c2 41.♕d6 ♕xd6 42.♖1xd6+-] 40.♖xe8+ ♔g7 41.♕d8 ♕f4 [41...♕xd8 42.♖dxd8+-] 42.♖g8+ ♔h6 43.♕h4+ ♖h5 44.♕xh5+ gxh5 45.g5+ ♕xg5 46.♖xg5 ♔xg5 47.♖c1 1-0

(44)

▷ G. Kamsky
► V. Akobian
USA Championship Saint Louis, 30.03.2017

22...♕xc4! [22...♖xd8 23.♗xd3±] 23.bxc4 [23.♕e5 ♕c3 24.♗c7 dxc2-+] 23...dxe2 24.♗b6 ♖e8 25.♘e1 ♗xa4 0-1

(45)

▷ M. Marin
► K. Lupulescu
Romanian Championship, 01.04.2017

50...e3?? [50...♕a7! 51.♕c1 ♕f2-+] 51.♖e7 e2 52.♖xe2 ♘e5+-

(46)

▷ C. Lupulescu
► V. Nevednichy
Romanian Championship, 02.04.2017

61.♗e6! ♔g8 [61...fxe6 62.♖b7++-; 61...♕h8 62.♕f2+-] 62.♗xf7+! [62. ♖b7 ♖b6+ 63.♖xb6 ♗xb6=] 62...♕xf7 63.♖b8+ ♕f8 64.♖xf8+ ♔xf8 65.♕h8+ ♔f7 66.♕xe5 1-0

(47)

▷ H. Nakamura
► A. Onischuk
USA Championship Saint Louis, 07.04.2017

33...♕g7! [33...♗xd5? 34.♖xd5! ♘xd5 35.♕e5+ ♔c8 36.♕xh8++-] 34.♘c3 ♕xf7 35.♕e5 ♖e8 36.♕d6 ♕f8∓

(48)

▷ S. Vidit
► M. Antipov
Dubai Open, 08.04.2017

35.♘xg6! ♖xf3 [35...fxg6 36.♖xf5 gxf5 37.♕xc5 ♕xc5 38.♖xc5+-] 36.♘e7+! ♗xe7 37.♕xc6 ♖f2+ 38.♔h3 ♖xe2 +-

(49)

▷ E. Iturrizaga Bonelli
▶ L. Pantsulaia
Dubai Open, 08.04.2017

21.exd6! [21.♗xg6 hxg6 22.exd6 ♗xd6 23.♖cd1+-] **21...♗xd6 22.♗xg6 hxg6 23.♖cd1 e5** [23...♕b8 24.♘b5+-] **24.♖xd6 exf4 25.♕d1 ♗xf3 26.♖xf3 ♘e5 27.♖xf4** +-

(50)

▷ K. Landa
▶ J. Van Foreest
Bundesliga, 09.04.2017

40.f5! ♕d3 [40...gxf5 41.♕xd5 exd5 42.♖f4#] **41.fxe6 ♕xg3+ 42.♔h1 ♕h3+ 43.♗h2** [43.♖h2? ♕f3+ 44.♖g2+ ♔h3–+] **43...♕xb3 44.exf7 ♕b1+ 45.♗g1 ♕e4+ 46.♖g2+ ♔xh4 47.♗f2+** 1–0

(51)

▷ A. Rakhmanov
▶ J. Santos Latasa
Dubai Open, 11.04.2017

28.♗f6! g6 [28...gxf6 29.exf6! ♔h8 30.♖h4 ♕e5 31.♕d3! h5 32.♕f3+-] **29.♕h3 h5 30.♖f5 ♖xf6 31.exf6 ♖d8 32.♖xh5 gxh5 33.♕xh5 ♖d4 34.♕g5+ ♔f8 35.♖e1** 1–0

(52)

▷ A. Smirnov
▶ M. Krasenkow
Doeberl Cup Canberra, 14.04.2017

38...♘f2+! [38...♕f5–+] **39.♔g1** [39. ♕xf2 ♕xb1+ 40.♖xb1 ♖xf2–+] **39... ♘h3+ 40.♔h1 ♕xf3** 0–1

(53)

▷ G. Antal
▶ E. Vorobiov
La Roda Open, 15.04.2017

18...♗xh3+!! 19.♔xh3 ♖f2! 20.♕h1 ♖af8 21.♘d2 ♕d7+ 22.♔g3 ♕d6+ 23.♔h3 ♖xd2 24.♖ae1 [24.♖f1 ♖xf1 25.♕xf1 ♕h2+ 26.♔g4 ♖f2–+] **24... ♖f3+ 25.♕xf3 ♖h2+ 26.♔g4 ♕g6+ 27.♔f4 ♖xh4+ 28.♔e5 ♖h5+** 0–1

(54)

▷ A. Seyb
▶ A. Graf
Karlsruhe Grenke Open, 17.04.2017

12.e5! fxe5 [12...♘xe5 13.♘xe5 fxe5 14.♘e4+-] **13.♘e4 ♗a7** [13...♔g7 14.♘xc5 dxc5 15.♖fe1+-] **14.♘f6 ♘ce7 15.♕d2 ♕c6 16.♘xe5 dxe5 17.♕d8+** +-

(55)

▷ M. Vachier Lagrave
▶ Y. Hou
Grenke Chess Classic, 19.04.2017

54.♗b4!! [54.bxa4? ♘c5 55.♗d2+ ♔xh5 56.a5 ♔g6 57.♗e3 ♘a6 58.♗b3 ♔f5 59.♔c4 ♔e6=] **54...♔xh5** [54...c5 55.bxa4! cxb4 56.axb4 ♔xh5 57.a5+-] **55.bxa4 ♘f6** [55...c5 56.a5!+-] **56.a5 ♘d5 57.a6 ♘c7 58.a7 ♔g6 59.♗a5**

♘a8 60.♔b3 ♔f7 61.♔c4 ♔e7 62.♔c5 ♔d7 63.♗b6 +-

(56)

▷ E. Rozentalis
► A. Brkic
Austrian League, 21.04.2017

46.c7! ♖xd2+ 47.♔c3! ♖d1 48.♖a2! 1-0

(57)

▷ B. Firat
► M. Kleinman
Reykjavik Open, 22.04.2017

20...♘d3+! 21.♔e2 [21.♔d2 ♘c6!! 22.♕xh7+ (22.♕e6+ ♔g7! (22...♔xf8 23.♔c2 ♔g7 24.♗e3 (24.♖d1 ♕f3 25.♗g5 ♕xf2+ 26.♖d2 ♘db4+!-+) 24...♘de5-+) 23.♘d7 (23.♔c2 ♘de5 24.♗e3 ♕e4+ 25.♔c1 ♕d3-+) 23...♘c5 24.♕f6+ ♔g8-+) 22...♔xf8 23.♕h8+ (23.♔c2 ♕e4 24.♗h6+ ♔e8 25.♕h8+ ♔f7-+) 23...♔f7 24.♕h7+ ♔e6-+] 21...♕g4+ 22.♔d2 [22.f3 ♕g2+ 23.♔e3 ♘c4+-+] 22...♘b4+ 0-1 [22...♘b4+ 23.♕xd8 ♘c4+ 24.♔e1 ♘c2#]

(58)

▷ A. Denk
► J. Nunn
World Championship Seniors 50, 25.04.2017

23...♕c7! 0-1 [23...♕c7 24.♖d1 ♘c6 (24...♖d8-+) 25.♕c3 ♗xe5 26.♘xe5 ♕xe5-+]

(59)

▷ D. Flores
► H. Van Riemsdijk
Szmetan Memorial Buenos Aires, 26.04.2017

15.♘b5! ♔b8 [15...a6 16.♘a7+ ♔c7 17.♘axc6+-] 16.♕xc6! f6 [16... ♖c8 17.♕d6+ ♕xd6 18.♘xd6 ♖c7 19.♖c1+-] 17.♘g6 ♕d7 [17... bxc6 18.♘xe7 cxb5 19.♘c6+ ♔b7 20.♘xd8+ ♖xd8 21.♗g6+-] 18.♕xd7 ♗xd7 19.♘xh8 ♖xh8 20.♘d6 1-0

(60)

▷ S. Movsesian
► M. Yilmaz
Reykjavik Open, 27.04.2017

43.♕c5! ♔e7 [43...♔d7 44.♕d5 ♔e7 45.♘a5+-] 44.♘xd6 ♘xd6 45.♕xe5+ ♔d7 46.♕d5 ♖xb3 [46...♖b6 47.♖xb6 ♕xb6 48.e5+-] 47.♖xd6+ +-

(61)

▷ N. Altini
► S. Brunello
Italian League, 30.04.2017

23...♖c8! 24.♖c1 [24.a3 ♖b7! 25.h3 ♖bc7-+] 24...♖xc4! 25.♖xc4 ♖b2 26.♖c8+ ♔g7 0-1 [26...♘xc8?? 27.♕xc8+ ♔g7 28.♕c5=]

[62]

▷ A. Grischuk
► B. Grachev
Russian League, 05.05.2017

34.♖b5!! ♖xa1 [34...axb5 35.♖xb1
♖b7 36.cxb5+-] **35.♖xb8 ♔f7 36.♕g3
♕d7 37.e5** +-

[63]

▷ A. Grischuk
► K. Alekseenko
Russian League, 08.05.2017

**33.♖xd5! ♖xd5 34.♕h6 ♘e6 35.♘e4
♖g8 36.♘f3 ♕f8 37.♘fg5 ♘xg5
38.♘xg5 ♖g7** [38...♕xh6 39.♘xf7#]
39.fxg7+ ♕xg7 40.♘xf7+ 1–0

[64]

▷ F. Vallejo Pons
► T. Radjabov
Fide GP Moscow, 15.05.2017

29...♗xc4! [29...♖d7? 30.f4!! ♗xc4
(*30...exf4 31.e5!*+-) 31.fxe5+-] **30.f4**
[30.dxc4 ♖d7!-+; 30.♘xf7+ ♗xf7-+]
**30...exf4 31.e5 ♕e7! 32.♘xf7+ ♗xf7
33.♖g1 ♗xa2** -+

[65]

▷ H. Stefansson
► G. Kjartansson
Icelandic Championship Hafnarf-
jordur, 15.05.2017

17...♗xh2+! 18.♔f1 [18.♔xh2 ♘g4+
19.♔g3 ♕g5 20.♗xh7+ ♔h8 21.♖xd5

♕xd5 22.♖h1 ♘f6 23.♗e4+ ♘h5+-+]
18...♗e5∓

[66]

▷ Y. Pelletier
► C. Vitoux
French League, 19.05.2017

12...♘xf3+! 13.♗xf3 ♕h4! 14.g3 [14.
h3 ♗xh3 15.gxh3 ♕xh3-+] **14...♕f6
15.♗xd5** [15.♗g2 ♗f5 16.e4 ♕xa1
17.exf5 ♖ac8-+] **15...♗f5 16.♗b2
♗xc2 17.♗xf6 gxf6** -+

[67]

▷ J. Xiong
► V. Akobian
Saint Louis Spring-A, 20.05.2017

28...♕g6! 29.♕xb7 [29.hxg4 ♕h6!
30.♖c2 (*30.♕d2 ♖f8 31.♖c1 ♖f2-+*)
30...♕xe3+ 31.♔g2 ♖f8 32.♕c3 ♖f2+
33.♔g1 ♕f4 34.♗g2 e3-+] **29...♖f8
30.♖c8 ♕f5** 0–1

[68]

▷ T. Sanikidze
► A. Sokolov
French League, 20.05.2017

26.♘e5! fxe5 [26...♖xd3 27.♘g6++-]
**27.♗xg8 ♗xg8 28.♖f3+ ♔e8
29.♕xg8+ ♔d7 30.♖d3+ ♔c7** [30...
♔c8 31.♖xd8+ ♕xd8 32.♕e6+±]
**31.♖xd8 ♕xd8 32.♕xg7+ ♔c6
33.♕xe5 c4 34.♕e4+ ♔c5 35.g4 b5
36.♕e3+** 1–0

(69)

▷ A. David
► M. Palac
French League, 21.05.2017

28.e6! ♖xe6 [28...fxe6 29.♘xg7 ♗xg7 30.♕g4+-] **29.♖xe6 ♕xe6 30.♖xb7 ♖d8 31.♗g5 ♖d5 32.♘e7+ ♗xe7 33.♖xe7 ♕c6 34.♕c2** 1-0 [34.♕c2 ♕xc2 35.♖e8#]

(70)

▷ A. David
► M. Cornette
French League, 25.05.2017

48...♗c7! 0-1 [48...♗c7 49.♕f3 ♖e1+ 50.♗g1 ♖xg1+ 51.♔xg1 ♕e1+-+]

(71)

▷ I. Nyzhnyk
► R. Li
Chicago Open, 29.05.2017

17.♘xd5! ♘xd5 [17...♕xd5 18.♕xd5 ♘xd5 19.♖xc5+-] **18.♕c2!** ♕h6 **19.♕xc5 ♗xh3 20.♖c4** +-

(72)

▷ S. Das
► Z. Rahman
Bhubaneswar Open, 29.05.2017

16...♗h6! 17.♕xh6 ♕xd4+ 18.♔h1 ♘xe5! [18...♕xa4? 19.♗xg6=] **19.♗xg6** [19.♕g5 ♘xd3 20.cxd3 ♕xa4 21.♕xe7 ♕f4∓] **19...♘xg6**

20.♘c3 ♕f2 21.h3 ♕xc2 22.♕e3 e5 0-1

(73)

▷ E. Sutovsky
► L. Paichadze
European Championship Minsk, 02.06.2017

24...♘g3+! 25.♕xg3 [25.fxg3 ♕xf3 26.gxf3 ♖xg3 27.♖e5 ♖g1+ 28.♔h2 ♖xf1-+] **25...♗xg3 26.fxg3 e5 27.♗a3 cxd4 28.cxd4 ♖xa6 29.bxa6 ♕b3** -+

(74)

▷ B. Dastan
► I. Saric
European Championship Minsk, 03.06.2017

36...♖e1+! 37.♖xe1 ♖xe1+ 38.♔h2 f4! 39.h4 [39.cxd6 ♘f1+ 40.♔g1 ♘g3+ 41.♔f2 ♖f1#] **39...♘f1+ 40.♔h3 ♘e3! 41.♖xe3** [41.cxd6 ♖h1#; 41.♔h2 ♘g4+ 42.♔h3 ♘f2+ 43.♔h2 ♖h1#] **41...♖xe3+ 42.♔g4 ♖d3 43.cxd6 ♖xd5 44.♔xf4 ♖xd6** -+

(75)

▷ V. Ivanchuk
► K. Piorun
Capablanca Memorial Matanzas, 04.06.2017

29...♘h5! 30.♘d7 ♘g3+ 31.♔xh2 ♖f5! 32.♖e1 [32.♔g1 ♖xd7 33.cxd7 ♕xd7-+] **32...♖xd7 33.♕g4+** [33. cxd7 ♕xd7 34.♕g4+ ♔h8 35.♖c3

♖h5+ 36.♔g1 ♕a7+ 37.♖c5 ♖f5!!–+]
33...♖g7 0–1

(76)

▷ **R. Ponomariov**
▶ **B. Macieja**
European Championship Minsk,
05.06.2017

27.♗xh6! ♗xb3 [27...gxh6 28.♕xh6
♘d7 29.♖e3 ♗xb3 30.f4+-] **28.axb3
gxh6 29.♕xh6 ♘h7 30.♖e4! f5** [30...
♘f8 31.♖g4+ ♘g6 32.h4+-] **31.♖xe6
♕b7 32.♖ce1! ♖c7 33.♖e8+ ♖xe8
34.♖xe8+ ♔f7 35.♕e6+** 1–0

(77)

▷ **S. Shankland**
▶ **V. Ivanchuk**
Capablanca Memorial Matanzas,
06.06.2017

38.e7! ♖xe2 39.♔f1! 1–0 [39.♖f8?
♖e1+ 40.♖f1 ♖xf1+ 41.♔xf1 ♘f6–+;
39.e8♕? ♖e1#; 39.♔f1 ♖f2+ 40.♔e1
♘f6 41.♖f8! ♖f4 42.e8♕ (42.♖xf6
♖e4=) 42...♘xe8 43.♖xf4+-]

(78)

▷ **P. Ponkratov**
▶ **R. Ponomariov**
European Championship Minsk,
06.06.2017

22...d6! 23.♗xd6 [23.exd6 ♕e1+
24.♔c2 ♗e4+-+; 23.♕xa6 ♕d7!
24.♗xd6 (24.exd6 ♗xg2 25.♗xg2
♖xc5+ 26.♔d2 ♕f5 27.♕a8+ ♖c8

28.♕e4 ♕a5+ 29.♔d1 ♕c3-+) 24...
♗b5+-+] **23...♕d7 24.♗c5 ♗b5
25.♕c2 ♗xf1 26.♖xf1 ♕b5 27.♕f2
♗f8** 0–1

(79)

▷ **E. Sutovsky**
▶ **D. Forcen Esteban**
European Championship Minsk,
08.06.2017

21.♘g6+! fxg6 22.hxg6 ♕e4 [22...
f4 23.♖xh6+ gxh6 24.g7+ ♔h7
25.gxf8♕+-; 22...♔g8 23.♗xh6 gxh6
24.♖xh6+-] **23.♗xh6** [23.♖xh6+
♔g8 24.♖h7+-] **23...♕g4 24.♗g5+**
1–0

(80)

▷ **D. Khismatullin**
▶ **D. Sadzikowski**
European Championship Minsk,
09.06.2017

**16.♘dxc4! bxc4 17.♘xc4 ♕c7 18.b4
a5 19.bxc5 ♘xc5 20.♘a3±**

(81)

▷ **A. Giri**
▶ **V. Anand**
Norway Chess Stavanger, 10.06.2017

32.g6! ♕d7 [32...♕xh4 33.gxf7+
♔h7 34.♔g2 ♕g5+ 35.♔f2+-; 32...
f5 33.♕h5 ♕g4+ 34.♕xg4 fxg4
35.♖e1+-] **33.♗b4!** 1–0 [33.♗b4 a5
34.♗a3 ♕e8 35.d4+-]

[82]

▷ G. Kaidanov
► E. Iturrizaga Bonelli
American Continental Medellin
Rapid, 18.06.2017

21...♗xg3! 22.hxg3 ♖h5+ [22...♘xb3
23.♕e3 ♖h5+ 24.♔g1 ♕c5∓] **23.♔g1
♘xb3! 24.♕e3 ♕c5 25.♕xc5 ♘xc5∓**

[83]

▷ F. Caruana
► E. Bacrot
Paris GCT Rapid, 22.06.2017

41...♕g4!! 42.h4 [42.♔h1 ♖d1+-
+; 42.♕f5 ♘h3+ 43.♔h1 ♘xf2+
44.♕xf2 ♖f8-+; 42.♘d5 ♕d1+ 43.♖f1
♕xf1#] **42...♘h3+ 43.♔h2 ♘xf2
44.♕e7 ♖f8 45.b6 ♗f1** 0–1

[84]

▷ A. Strikovic
► S. Del Rio de Angelis
Sanxenxo Carlos Open, 23.06.2017

24.b4! ♕a3 [24...cxb3 25.♖xa6+-]
25.♘c5 ♕xc3 26.♖xa6 1–0

[85]

▷ E. Bacrot
► W. So
Paris GCT Blitz, 24.06.2017

39...♖bc4? [39...♖a4! 40.♖7d2 (40.
f4+ ♔f6 41.g4 h6=) 40...♖a1 41.♖e2+
♔f6 42.♖de1 ♖axb1 43.♖xe6+=]
40.♔f1 ♖a4 41.♖e1+ ♔f6 42.♖dd1
1–0

[86]

▷ S. Mamedyarov
► F. Caruana
Paris GCT Blitz, 25.06.2017

44...♖d7+? [44...e3+! 45.♔e2 (45.fxe3?
♕g2+ 46.♕e2 (46.♔d3 ♕f1+ 47.♖e2
♖d7+-+) 46...♖d7+-+) 45...exf2+
46.♔xf2 ♕h2+ 47.♔f3 ♕h5+ 48.♔g4
♕h1+ 49.♔g3 (49.♔f2 ♕h2+=) 49...
♕g1+ 50.♔h3 ♕h1+=] **45.♔e3 ♕e1+
46.♔f4 ♗e5+ 47.♔xe5 ♕a5+ 48.♕c5**
1–0

[87]

▷ F. Caruana
► A. Grischuk
Paris GCT Blitz, 25.06.2017

19...dxc4! 20.dxc4 [20.bxc4 ♘a4–+]
20...♘xb3! 21.♕xb3 [21.♖ad1 ♘xd4
22.♖xd4 ♕c5–+] **21...♕xd4+ –+**

[88]

▷ L'Ami,E
► L. Van Wely
Dutch Championship Amsterdam,
27.06.2017

21.♕xf7+!! ♗xf7 22.♘xf7 ♕c7
[22...♕b6 23.♘xg5+ ♔h8 24.♘f7+
♔g8 25.♘xd6+ ♔h8 26.♘f7+ ♔g8
27.a3+-] **23.♘xg5+ ♔h8 24.♘f7+
♔g8 25.♘xd6+ ♔h8 26.♘f7+ ♔g8
27.♖d8! +-**

(89)

▷ B. Bok
▶ J. Van Foreest
Dutch Championship Amsterdam,
27.06.2017

21...♗e5! 22.♕h4 ♕e6! 23.♖ac1
[23.♖f1 ♗d4–+] 23...♗xg3! [23...
♗b2 24.♖e4 ♕xa2–+] 24.♖e4 [24.
♕xg3 ♕xe3+ 25.♕f2 ♖d1+ 26.♖xd1
♖xd1+ 27.♔g2 ♖g5+ 28.♕g3 ♖xg3+
29.♔xg3 ♖d2–+] 24...♕h3 0–1 [24...
♕h3 25.hxg3 ♖d1+–+]

(90)

▷ S. Ernst
▶ T. Burg
Dutch Championship Amsterdam,
30.06.2017

24.♘xf7! ♕c7 [24...♔xf7 25.♕h5+
♔g8 (25...♔e7 26.d5+–) 26.♕g6
♘e7 27.♕h7+ ♔f7 28.♗xb7 ♖b8
29.d5+–] 25.♘xh6+ gxh6 26.d5! ♘d4
27.♗xd4 exd5 28.♕g4+ ♗g7 29.♗f5
♖b8 30.♕g6 ♔f8 31.♗e6 ♖e7 32.♖c3
♗xd4 33.♕g8# 1–0

(91)

▷ F. Peralta
▶ L. Henderson de la Fuente
Montcada Open, 01.07.2017

20...♘h5! 21.♕g5 ♘xd3 22.♕xh5
♗xf5 23.♕xf5 ♕c2 0–1 [23...♕c2
24.♗b2 ♘f2+–+]

(92)

▷ L. Ljubojevic
▶ J. Timman
Platja d'Aro Legends Blitz, 01.07.2017

33...♖xf2? [33...dxc3! 34.♕xc2 ♖xd1+
35.♕xd1 c2 36.♕c1 ♕d6–+] 34.♖xb6?
[34.♗d2=] 34...♕xb6 35.♗xd4 ♖xb2
36.♗xb6 ♖xd3 37.♖xd3 axb6–+

(93)

▷ S. Atalik
▶ O. Sahin
Nis Open, 04.07.2017

24.♕f3! ♘xe4 [24...♕h7 25.♖h1
♕xg7 26.♔d2+–; 24...♖xg7
25.♖xg7+ ♔xg7 26.♔d2+–; 24...fxe4
25.♕xf7++–] 25.♖h1 ♘g5 [25...♕f6
26.♖h8+ ♔xg7 27.♕h5+–] 26.♕g2
♕xh1+ [26...♕g4 27.♕xg4 fxg4
28.♗xg5+–] 27.♕xh1 ♖xg7 28.♗xg5
♖xg5 29.♔d2 1–0

(94)

▷ L. Van Wely
▶ A. David
Greek League, 07.07.2017

59.♕f8+! ♔g5 60.♕e7+? [60.h4+!!
♔h5 (60...♔xh4?? 61.♕h6#) 61.♕h8+
♔g6 62.♕g8+ ♔f6 63.♕f8+=] 60...
♔h5 61.♕xe5+ ♔h6 62.♕xf4+ ♔g6
63.♕g3+ ♔f6 64.♕h4+ ♔f7–+

(95)

▷ T. Radjabov
▶ P. Eljanov
Fide GP Geneva, 07.07.2017

35.♖g4! ♔f8 [35...♔h8 36.♘f6+-;
35...♕xd5 36.♖xe8+ ♖xe8 37.♕xd5+-
; 35...♖xe4 36.♘f6++-] **36.♖ef4** [36.
♖xg7! ♖xe4 (36...♔xg7 37.♕c3+ f6
38.♘xf6+-) 37.♖g8+! ♔xg8 38.♘f6+
♔g7 39.♘xd7 ♖e6 40.♕g4+ ♔h7
41.♘e5!+-] **36...♗d6** [36...♖ed8
37.♖xf7+ ♕xf7 38.♖f4 ♖d7 39.♖xf7+
♖xf7 40.♘f4 ♔g8 41.♕d5+-] **37.♖d4**
[37.♖xg7! ♗xf4 38.♖g8++-] **37...♕b7**
38.♖xg7! ♗e5 [38...♔xg7 39.♖g4+
♔f8 40.♖g8+ ♔xg8 41.♘f6+ ♔f8
42.♕xb7 ♖c7 43.♕d5 ♖e6 44.♕a8+
♔g7 45.♘e8++-] **39.♖g8+** ♔xg8
40.♘f6+ ♗xf6 **41.♖g4+** 1–0

(96)

▷ I. Nepomniachtchi
▶ Y. Hou
Fide GP Geneva, 09.07.2017

36.♗g5!! [36.♗xd4 g5=] **36...♖f8**
37.♖f4 ♔e6 [37...♔e8 38.♗xf6+-]
38.♕g4+ ♔d6 **39.e5+!** ♔c7 [39...
♕xe5 40.♖xd4+ ♔e7 41.♖e3+-]
40.♗xf6 ♖xf6 **41.exf6** +-

(97)

▷ D. Debashis
▶ F. Sieber
Najdorf Memorial Warsaw,
09.07.2017

18.b4! ♘xf2 [18...♘xb4 19.♘xb4
♗xb4 20.♕d4+-] **19.♔xf2 d4 20.bxc5**
dxe3+ 21.♔g1 bxc5 22.♕e2 1–0

(98)

▷ D. Bocharov
▶ V. Artemiev
Russian Higher League Sochi,
09.07.2017

30...♖xe3! 31.♖xd3 [31.♗xe3
♕xd1+-+] **31...♖xc1+** 0–1

(99)

▷ Y. Hou
▶ R. Rapport
Fide GP Geneva, 10.07.2017

28...♗xg2+! 29.♘xg2 [29.♔e2
♗xh3-+] **29...f3!** [29...♖xg2? 30.♔e2
♗h4 31.♖f1 ♔g6∓] **30.♗e3 e4!** [30...
♖xg2 31.♔e1 ♔g6∓] **31.♖a3 ♗e5** [31...
♗xb2 32.♖b3 ♗e5 33.♖xb7 ♔h8-+]
32.♖b3 c6 33.♗d4 fxg2+ 34.♔g1
♖d8 -+

(100)

▷ R. Ponomariov
▶ V. Malakhov
Danzhou, 16.07.2017

28.f6! ♗xf6 **29.♕d3 ♖ad8 30.♗xe4**
♕c8 31.♕c3±

(101)

▷ H. Martirosyan
► H. Gabuzyan
Lake Sevan Martuni, 16.07.2017

40.♗h3? [40.♖xd5! g5+ (40...♘xd5 41.♕f7+ ♔h8 42.♕g8#) 41.♖xg5+ hxg5+ 42.♕xg5++–] **40...♕e1!!** **41.♗e6** [41.g4 g5+–+; 41.♗g4 g5+ 42.♖xg5+ hxg5+ 43.♕xg5+ ♔f7 44.♗f5 ♖c6 45.♕g6+ ♔f8 46.♕h6+ ♔e8–+; 41.♖xe1 g5+–+] **41...♕h1!** **42.g4 ♖c3** [42...♖c6–+] **43.g5 hxg5+** **44.♖xg5 ♕e4 45.♕xe4 ♘xe4 –+**

(102)

▷ A. Hauchard
► M. Demidov
Pardubice Rapid Open, 20.07.2017

34...♖cf8! 35.e4 ♖8f3! 36.♗xf3 ♘xf3 **37.♗f4 ♘xe1 38.♖xe1 ♖xf4 –+**

(103)

▷ D. Paravyan
► K. Bryzgalin
Pardubice Open, 23.07.2017

17.a5! ♕xb2 [17...♕c5 18.♗xe6 ♘xe6 19.♗d6+–] **18.♖a2 ♕xa2 19.♗xa2** **♗xa2 20.c4! ♖e8 21.♕c2** 1–0

(104)

▷ F. Urkedal
► I. Sokolov
Helsingor Xtracon Open, 25.07.2017

18.♖xg7+! [18.♕xc6±] **18...♔f8** [18...♔xg7 19.♕g2+ ♔f8 20.♕g5+–] **19.♕g2** 1–0

(105)

▷ R. Yu
► A. Moiseenko
Chinese League, 26.07.2017

28...♗a3!! 29.♗c3 [29.♖b1 ♗b3+ 30.♔c3 (30.♔c1 ♖c8+–+) 30...♗a2–+; 29.bxa3 ♗b3+ 30.♔c1 ♖c8+ 31.♗c2 ♖xc2+ 32.♔b1 f4–+] **29...♗b3+** **30.♔d2 ♗xd1 31.bxa3 ♗b3 î s**

(106)

▷ A. Brkic
► V. Bukal
Pardubice Open, 26.07.2017

21.♕h5! gxh5 22.♖g3 1–0 [22.♖g3 ♖d8 23.♖xg7+ ♔f8 24.♗xh7+–]

(107)

▷ A. Liang
► R. Praggnanandhaa
Saint Louis Millennials U14,
28.07.2017

28...♗a6! 29.♕b6 [29.♕a4 ♖fb8 30.b4 axb4 31.axb4 ♗e2 32.♕xa8 ♘f3+–+] **29...♘c8 30.♕xa5 ♗e2** 0–1 [30...♗e2 31.♕xa8 ♘f3+–+]

(108)

▷ E. Safarli
► L. Pantsulaia
Turkish League, 29.07.2017

39.♖xf5! gxf5 40.♕h4 ♕f8 [40...
♔g6 41.♕g3+ ♔xf6 42.♕h4++-]
**41.♕xh5+ ♕h6 42.♕xf5+ ♕g6
43.♕e5** [43.♕f4! ♕b1+ 44.♔f2
♕c2+ 45.♔g3 ♕g6+ 46.♔h4 ♕h6+
47.♕xh6+ ♔xh6 48.♗e4 ♖a6 49.g4
♖xf6 50.g5++-] **43...♕b1+** [43...♕g4
44.♔f2+-] **44.♔f2 ♕c2+ 45.♔g3
♕d3+ 46.♔h4** 1–0

[109]

▷ M. Vachier Lagrave
► W. So
Sinquefield Cup Saint Louis,
02.08.2017

41.♗e4! ♘xb3+ [41...♘xb6 42.♗xd4
cxd4 43.♗xb7 ♖b8 44.♗xa6+-]
42.♔c3 ♘d4 43.♗h2! 1–0 [43.
♗h2 ♘xb6 (43...♘c6 44.♗c7++-)
44.♗xb7+-]

[110]

▷ H. Tikkanen
► I. Saric
Lund CellaVision Cup, 05.08.2017

21...♘h3+!! 22.♔f1 [22.gxh3 ♕g5+
23.♔f1 ♗a6+-+] **22...♗a6+ 23.c4
♖d8** 0–1 [23...♖d8 24.♕xg7+ ♕xg7
25.♘xg7 ♗xc4+ 26.♔e1 ♖f8-+]

[111]

▷ R. Svane
► G. Meier
German Masters Dresden,
05.08.2017

26.♖xf7! [26.♗xf7+ ♔f8 27.♖xd7
♖xd7 28.♗xe8 ♔xe8±] **26...c4
27.♖xd7** [27.♗xc4 ♖xc4-+] **27...
♖xd7 28.♗xc4+!** [28.♗a4 ♖ee7
29.♗xd7 ♖xd7±] **28...♔f8 29.♗b5
♖d2 30.♗xe8 ♔xe8 31.♗a1** 1–0

[112]

▷ C. Sochacki
► A. Dgebuadze
Charleroi Open, 05.08.2017

9...♘c5! 10.gxf4 [10.d4 ♘xe4 11.♗c4∓
(11.gxf4 ♕a5+ 12.♘c3 ♘xc3-+)] **10...
♘d3+ 11.♔e2** [11.♗xd3 ♕xd3 12.♕e2
♕xf3 13.♕xf3 ♗xf3 14.0-0 ♗xe4-+]
11...f5 12.♔e3 [12.exf5 ♕d5 13.♗g2
♘xf4+ 14.♔f1 ♕d3+ 15.♔g1 ♘e2+
16.♔h2 ♗xf3 17.♗xf3 ♕xf3-+] **12...
fxe4 13.♗c3 e5 14.fxe5 ♗c5+ 15.♗d4
♗xd4+ 16.♘xd4 ♕g5+** 0–1

[113]

▷ M. Carlsen
► M. Vachier Lagrave
Sinquefield Cup Saint Louis,
05.08.2017

50...axb6! [50...♘c1+ 51.♔a3 axb6
52.♗c6 ♗e4 53.a7 ♖d8 54.♘d6+ ♖xd6
55.♗xe4 ♖d8 56.a8♕ ♖xa8+ 57.♗xa8
♘d3 58.♔a4=] **51.♗c6 ♗e4!! 52.a7**
[52.♗xd5+ ♗xd5 53.b3 f4-+] **52...
♖d8 53.♘d6+ ♖xd6 54.♗xe4 ♖d8
55.a8♕** [55.♗xd3 ♔f6-+] **55...♖xa8+
56.♗xa8 ♘e5** -+

(114)

▷ E. Vorobiov
▶ I. Semjonovs
Riga Tech Open, 07.08.2017

24.♕b2‼ ♖b7 [24...♔g8 25.b4 ♘a4
26.♕a3+-] **25.b4 ♘d5 26.♘xd5+ ♔g8
27.♘f6+ ♔f7 28.♘xh7** 1–0

(115)

▷ L. Aronian
▶ W. So
Sinquefield Cup Saint Louis,
08.08.2017

29.♖f6‼ h5 [29...♔f8 30.♖g6! ♕c3
31.e5 ♕xd3 32.♖xg7+-] **30.♖h6! ♕c3
31.♖xh5 g6 32.e5!** 1–0 [32.e5 ♕xd3
33.♕h4 gxh5 34.♕xd8++-]

(116)

▷ M. Ulybin
▶ A. Czajkowski
Suwalki Warakomska Memorial,
11.08.2017

19.♗f4! ♕c5 20.♕xf6! 1–0 [20.♕xf6
gxf6 21.♗h6#]

(117)

▷ R. Ponomariov
▶ D. Forcen Esteban
Spanish Championship Rapid Lin-
ares, 13.08.2017

23.♕h3? [23.♖xf6+‼ ♔xf6 24.♘xd5+
exd5 25.♕g6+ ♔e7 26.♗h4++-] **23...**

♖h8 24.♕g2 ♖h7 25.♖xf6+ gxf6
26.♕g6+ ♔e7 27.♕xh7+ +-

(118)

▷ L. Perez Rodriguez
▶ B. Sambuev
Quebec Open, 13.08.2017

22...♘f4! 23.♕d2 ♘e2+! 0–1 [23...
♘e2+ 24.♕xe2 (24.♔h1 ♘xc1
25.♖xc1 ♕xd2 26.N1xd2 ♗xb2–+)
24...♕xd1–+]

(119)

▷ T. Laurusas
▶ V. Kunin
Riga Tech Open, 13.08.2017

14.cxd5! exd5 [14...hxg5 15.dxe6 ♕xe6
(15...♗xg2 16.exf7++-) 16.♗xb7+-]
15.♗xf6 gxf6 [15...♕xf6 16.♘xd5 ♕d6
17.♘xc7+-] **16.♗xd5 ♗xd5 17.♘xd5
♕d6 18.♘g4 ♗g7 19.♘ge3**+-

(120)

▷ E. Iturrizaga Bonelli
▶ R. Ponomariov
Spanish League, 14.08.2017

**21...♘xd4‼ 22.♕xd4 ♘f5 23.♕f4 g5
24.♕d2 ♗xe5 25.♗h5 ♕f6! 26.♖ab1**
[26.♗xe8 ♖xe8 27.♖ab1 ♘d4 28.♖c3
♘xb5–+] **26...♖ec8 27.♖e1 ♗d4
28.♘d3 ♘g7 29.♗g4 ♖c4 30.♗d6
♗c3** 0–1

[121]

▷ L. Aronian
▶ D. Navara
Saint Louis Rapid, 14.08.2017

24.♖e4! ♖e7 [24...♕e7 25.♖g4+
♗g7 (25...♔h8 26.♗e4+-) 26.♗e4+-]
25.♖g4+ ♔h8 [25...♗g7 26.♗e4+-]
**26.♗e4 ♖c8 27.♖h4 ♔g8 28.♖xh7
♗xd5 29.♕g6+ ♖g7 30.♕h5 ♗xe4
31.♖h8#** 1–0

[122]

▷ A. Areshchenko
▶ T. Banusz
Spanish League, 14.08.2017

33.♗g5! e4 [33...fxg5 34.♖xf7+ ♔h6
(34...♔g8 35.♕f3+-) 35.♖1f6++-]
34.♗xf6+ ♗xf6 35.♖xf6 exd3 [35...
♕xf6 36.♖xf6 ♔xf6 37.♗xe4+-]
36.♖xf7+ ♔g8 37.♕xd3 +-[37.♕f3!
♗d7 38.d6+-]

[123]

▷ L. Martinez Duany
▶ J. Santos Latasa
Spanish League, 15.08.2017

28.♖xe5! ♖f8 [28...♖xe5 29.♕xf7+
♔h8 30.♘xg6+ ♔h7 31.♘xe5+-]
29.♘xg6 [29.♖e6!! fxe6 30.♕xe6+
♔h7 31.♕xg6+ ♔g8 32.♘hf5 ♖xf5
33.♕e6+! ♔h8 34.♘f7++-] **29...
♕xd6 30.♕xd6 ♖xd6 31.♘e7+ ♔h7
32.♖xc5±**

[124]

▷ O. Barbosa
▶ E. Perelshteyn
Washington Open, 15.08.2017

19.c5! bxc5 20.♘xf7!! ♕xd4 [20...
♖xf7 21.♖xe6+-; 20...♕c6 21.♕h3+-]
21.♕xd4 ♗xd4 22.♗xe6 +-

[125]

▷ A. Demchenko
▶ S. Movsesian
Spanish League, 19.08.2017

48.♔d4! ♖f5 [48...♖e6 49.♖xd5+-;
48...♖be8 49.bxc6 ♗b3 50.♖xe5 ♖xe5
51.♖b2 ♖d5+ 52.♔xe4+-] **49.g4 hxg4
50.♗xg4 ♖d8 51.♗xf5 ♗b3+ 52.♔e3
♗xc2 53.♖xc6+ ♔b7 54.♗xg6** +-

[126]

▷ S. Vidit
▶ A. Areshchenko
Spanish League, 20.08.2017

34.♖b8!! f3+ [34...♕xb8 35.♕a1++-]
35.♔h1 1–0

[127]

▷ A. Fawzy
▶ P. Maghsoodloo
Abu Dhabi Open, 21.08.2017

19.f5! ♘xe5 [19...exf5 20.e6+-; 19...
gxf5 20.♕h5 ♘h6 21.♘xe6 ♗xe5
22.♗xe5+-; 19...♗xe5 20.fxe6 fxe6
21.♘f7+-] **20.fxe6 f6** [20...fxe6
21.♘xe6 ♕b7 22.♘xg7+ ♕xg7

23.♕e2+-] **21.♗xe5 fxe5 22.♖f7 ♗f8**
[22...♗f6 23.♕f1+-] **23.♘xh7** [23.
♕f1!+-] 23...♗c5+ 24.♔h1 ♘e7 [24...
♗e7 25.♕f1 ♘h6 26.b6 ♔d8 27.♕b5
♕b7 28.♖f1 ♖xh7 29.♖a1+-] **25.♕f1
♘f5 26.b6 ♕c6 27.b7 ♗a7 28.♕xf5
gxf5 29.♘f6+ ♔d8 30.e7+** 1–0 [30.
e7+ ♔c7 31.e8♕+ ♔b6 32.♕xh8+-]

[128]

▷ **B. Amin**
▶ **S. Salem**
Abu Dhabi open, 21.08.2017

19.♘xg7! ♘g4 [19...♔xg7 20.♕xh6+
♔g8 21.♕g5+ ♔h8 22.dxc4+-]
20.♘xe6 ♗xf2+ [20...♘xf2 21.♘xd8
♘e4+ 22.♔h2 ♘xd2 23.♘xc6 ♕xc6
24.dxc4+-] **21.♔h1 ♗xg3 22.♘xd8
♗d5 23.♘xc6 ♕xc6 24.♖f1 ♘h2
25.♖f5** 1–0

[129]

▷ **F. Berkes**
▶ **P. Schlosser**
Schwarzach Open, 26.08.2017

23.♘xd5! exd5 24.♕xd5 ♗g6 [24...g6
25.g4 ♖d8 26.♕f3 ♗c8 27.♘a4 bxa4
28.♖xc6+-] **25.♘xb7 ♕xb7 26.♗f3**
1–0

[130]

▷ **G. Kamsky**
▶ **A. Sarana**
St. Petersburg Rapid, 27.08.2017

28.♘xg6+! hxg6 29.♕xg6 ♘f5 [29...
♘e8 30.♕h5+ ♔g8 31.f5+-] **30.♖xe6
♘xe6 31.♕xf5 ♘g7 32.♕g6 f5
33.♖xe7 ♗xe7 34.♘e3 ♖c6 35.♕f7
♗a3 36.♘xd5** 1–0

[131]

▷ **A. Demuth**
▶ **P. Duboue**
French Championship Accession
Agen, 27.08.2017

18.♘xf7! ♖xf7 [18...♗xh2+ 19.♔h1
♘a6 20.♘xh6+ gxh6 21.♗a3+-]
**19.♕e8+ ♗f8 20.♗a3 ♕d7 21.♖ae1
b6 22.♖xf7** 1–0 [22.♖xf7 ♕xf7
23.♕xf7+ ♔xf7 24.♖f1++-]

[132]

▷ **H. Wang**
▶ **D. Sengupta**
Fide World Cup Tbilisi, 04.09.2017

**32.h5! ♗h7 33.♖d8+ ♘xd8
34.♖xd8+ ♔e7 35.♖h8 ♘c5 36.♖xh7
♖xh5 37.♖xg7** +-

[133]

▷ **V. Plat**
▶ **P. Stoma**
Polish League, 04.09.2017

17.♗xh7+! ♔xh7 18.♘a4! ♕a5 [18...
♗xa4 19.♖xc4++-] **19.♖xc4+ ♔h8
20.♖xc8 ♗xc8 21.♘ac3** +-

(134)

▷ I. Ivanisevic
► V. Sanal
Serbian League, 06.09.2017

20.♞xf7! ♛xf7 [20...♚xf7 21.♛xg6+ ♚f8 22.♜xd7 ♛xd7 23.♗xh5+-] **21.♜xd7‼ ♛xd7 22.♛xg6+ ♚f8 23.♗xh5 ♜xh5 24.♛xh5 ♛d3 25.♛h6+ ♚e7 26.♜g7+ ♚d6 27.♛f4+ e5 28.♞e4+ 1-0**

(135)

▷ A. Motylev
► A. Giri
Fide World Cup Tbilisi, 08.09.2017

17...g5! 18.♗g3 ♞xe4 19.♜xe4 [19. ♜a3 ♞xg3 20.♜xg3 ♗xd5 21.♛xd5∓] **19...♗xd5 20.♛xd5 ♗xa1 21.c4 bxc4 22.♜xc4∓**

(136)

▷ V. Ivanchuk
► J. Duda
Fide World Cup Tbilisi, 08.09.2017

15.♞xd5 ♛xd2+ 16.♚xd2 cxd5 17.♗xa6 bxc5 18.♗c7 cxd4? [18...♜a8 19.♗b7±] **19.exd4 ♜a8 20.♗b7 +-**

(137)

▷ D. Bocharov
► S. Khanin
Kurnosov Memorial Rapid, 10.09.2017

19...♛f6! 20.♛c2 [20.♜c2 ♛h6 21.h3 ♞xe3 22.fxe3 ♛xe3+ 23.♚h2

♗xd4-+] **20...♛h6 21.♞f5** [21. h4 ♞xe3 22.fxe3 ♛xe3+ 23.♛f2 ♗xd4-+] **21...♛xh2+ 22.♚f1 ♗a6+ 0-1**

(138)

▷ M. Matlakov
► L. Aronian
Fide World Cup Tbilisi, 11.09.2017

26.♗xc5+! ♗xc5 27.♞d5+ ♜xd5 [27... ♚f8 28.♞xf6! ♜xd2 29.♞xh7+ ♚e7 30.♜xd2+-] **28.♜xd5 ♗c2 29.♜e1+ ♚f8 30.♜d7 1-0**

(139)

▷ L. Ding
► S. Vidit
Fide World Cup Tbilisi, 11.09.2017

19.d5! [19.dxc5±] **19...cxd5** [19... exd5 20.♗xf6+-] **20.♗xf6 g6** [20... ♗xf6 21.♛xh7+ ♚f8 22.♜xe6!+-] **21.♛b2+-**

(140)

▷ R. Rapport
► E. Najer
Fide World Cup Tbilisi, 14.09.2017

45...♞b4? [45...♜e1+! 46.♚g2 ♞b4 47.♜xa5 ♜e2+ 48.♚f1 ♜e1+ 49.♚g2 (49.♚f2? ♞xd3+-+) 49...♜e2+=] **46.♜e2 ♞xd3 47.f5! ♜xe2 48.fxg6+ ♚g7 49.♚xe2 ♞c1+ 50.♗xc1 1-0**

(141)

▷ M. Parligras
► K. Georgiev
Serbian League, 18.09.2017

19.♘xe6! fxe6 20.♕xe6+ ♔h8
21.♗xf6 ♘xf6 [21...gxf6 22.♗xb7
♕xb7 23.♖cd1+-] 22.♕xc8 ♖axc8
23.♗xb7 ♖c7 24.♗f3 +-

(142)

▷ L. Aronian
► M. Vachier Lagrave
Fide World Cup Tbilisi, 21.09.2017

54...♖a8?? [54...♖aa4!! 55.♖f1+ **a)**
55.♔h7 ♖h4+ 56.♔g7 ♖ag4+ 57.♔f7
♖h7+ 58.♔f8 (*58.♔e8?? ♖g8#*) 58...
♖h8+=; **b)** 55.e7?? ♖g6+ 56.♔h5 ♖g5+
57.♔h6 ♖h4#; 55...♖gf4 56.♖xf4+
♖xf4 57.♖xa2 ♔xe6=] **55.♖f1+ ♔f4
56.♖xf4+ ♔xf4 57.♖xa2 ♖xa2
58.e7+-**

(143)

▷ H. Gretarsson
► J. Ragnarsson
Reykjavik Taflfelag Open, 22.09.2017

10.♗f4! ♕c8 [10...e5 11.dxe5 ♘d5
12.♘xd5 cxd5 13.e6+-] 11.♕e2 e5 [11...
♗g6 12.♘d6++-] 12.♗xe5 ♘xe5
13.dxe5 ♕f5 14.exf6+ ♔d7 15.g4 ♕g6
16.♘e5+ 1–0

(144)

▷ M. Carlsen
► J. Granda Zuniga
Douglas IoM Open, 27.09.2017

21.♘g6+! fxg6 22.♖xe6 ♘xh7 [22...
♖xe6 23.♖xe6 ♘xh7 24.♖xd6 ♘f6
25.♕xg6 ♕xd6 26.♗b4+-] 23.♖xe8+
♖xe8 24.♖xe8+ ♔xe8 25.♕xg6+
♔d8 26.♕xh7 ♕e7 27.g3 ♔c7
28.♕g6 1–0

(145)

▷ F. Caruana
► G. Jones
Douglas IoM Open, 29.09.2017

23.♘fg5! ♖f5 [23...hxg5 24.♕h5+ ♔g8
25.♘xg5+-; 23...♖e7 24.♕g4 ♕d7
(*24...♕e8 25.♔h2!+-*) 25.♕xd7 ♖xd7
26.♘xd6+-] 24.♘e6 ♕d7 25.♕g4
♕f7 [25...♕xe6 26.♘g3+-] 26.♖xc7
♖xc7 27.♘xd6 ♖xf2 28.♘xc7 ♕f6
29.♘xd5 ♕xd4 30.♕xd4 ♗xd4
31.♖e4 ♗a7 32.♘b6 1–0

(146)

▷ R. Wojtaszek
► J. Tomczak
Polish League, 01.10.2017

36.♕e4! ♘c7 [36...♖c8 37.♘xg6
hxg6 38.♕xe6+ ♔f8 39.♕xc8+-]
37.♘xg6 f5 [37...hxg6 38.♕xg6+ ♔f8
39.♕xf6++-] 38.♘e7+ ♔f7 39.♕h4
h6 40.♕xh6 ♕b7+ 41.f3 1–0

(147)

▷ W. Spoelman
► R. Edouard
Belgian League, 01.10.2017

17...d5!! 18.c6 [18.cxd6 fxe3–+; 18.exd5
fxe3 19.♕xe3 ♘xc5–+] **18...dxc4
19.cxb7 ♖ad8 20.♕c2 fxe3 21.♕xc4
♕f7 22.♖xd8 ♘xd8** 0–1

(148)

▷ V. Malakhov
► V. Fedoseev
European Club Cup Antalya,
10.10.2017

**52.d7! ♖h3+ 53.♔d2 ♖h2+ 54.♔c3
♖h3+ 55.♔b2 ♖h2+ 56.♔a1 ♖d2
57.♖a5+ ♔b4 58.♖d5! exd5 59.d8♕
d4 60.c5 d3 61.c6** 1–0

(149)

▷ M. Ulybin
► G. Quparadze
Stavanger Open, 11.10.2017

49...♗b5! [49...♗c4–+] **50.♘f6+
♕xf6 51.♕xf6 ♖xa2+ 52.♔e1 ♖a1+
53.♔f2 ♖f1+ 54.♖xf1 gxf6 55.♖g1+
♔f8 56.♔e1** [56.♖c1 exd5–+] **56...b3**
0–1

(150)

▷ L. Krysa
► P. Acosta
Argentinian Championship Buenos
Aires, 15.10.2017

18.♘xf7! ♕xd4 [18...♔xf7 19.♕xe6#]
**19.♗e3! ♕d7 20.♗a4 ♕c7 21.♗xe8
bxc3 22.♘g5 ♕e5 23.♗f7+ ♔g7
24.♗d4** 1–0

(151)

▷ J. Bergthorsson
► J. Hjartarson
Islandic League, 19.10.2017

**19...♘xb4! 20.axb4 ♗xf3 21.gxf3
♖xc4** 0–1 [21...♖xc4 22.♗xc4 ♕g5+
23.♔h1 ♕g2#]

(152)

▷ B. Jobava
► J. Hammer
Swedish League, 20.10.2017

35...♕c1+? [35...♗xb3!! 36.h8♕ (36.
axb3 ♕c1+ 37.♔a4 ♕a1+ 38.♔b4
♕e1+ 39.♔c4 ♕c1+=) 36...♕xa2+
37.♔b4 ♕d2+ 38.♔xb3 ♕d1+ 39.♔b4
♕b1+=] **36.♔a4 ♗xb3+** [36...♕d2
37.♕c8+ ♔e7 38.♕b7+ ♔e6 39.a3
c5 40.♕b6 ♔d7 41.♕a7+ ♔e6 42.b4
♕d3 43.♕b8 ♕b3+ 44.♔a5 ♕xa3+
45.♔b6 ♕xb4+ 46.♔a7+–] **37.♔a5!**
1–0 [37.♔a5 ♕a3+ (37...♕e1+ 38.♔b6
♕xh4 39.♕c8++–) 38.♔b6 ♕b4+
39.♔a7+–]

(153)

▷ A. Goganov
► B. Jobava
Swedish League, 21.10.2017

33...♘g6! 0–1 [33...♔h6∓; 33...♘g6 34.♘xg6 (34.♘xc6 gxh4+ 35.♔h3 ♖xf3#) 34...♖xf3#]

(154)

▷ E. Cuberli
► D. Flores
Argentine Championship Buenos Aires, 22.10.2017

21...♘xc4! 22.hxg6 hxg6 23.♕xc4 ♕f5! 24.♔g2 ♕xb1 25.e4 b3 26.axb3 ♕xb3 27.♕a6 ♕b6 0–1

(155)

▷ F. Rambaldi
► L. Bruzon Batista
Saint Louis Spice Cup Open, 25.10.2017

30...♘xg2! 31.♗xd5 [31.♖xf8 ♖xf8 32.♔xg2 (32.♕xb4 ♖f5 33.♔xg2 ♖xf2+–+) 32...♗xh3+–+; 31.♔xg2 ♖xf3 32.♔xf3 ♕xh3+ 33.♔e2 ♗g4+ 34.f3 ♕xf3#] 31...♘xe1 32.♖f6 g4 33.hxg4 ♗xd5 34.♔f1 ♗c4+ 0–1

(156)

▷ S. Golubov
► S. Sjugirov
Chigorin Memorial St. Petersburg, 25.10.2017

24...♘f4!! 25.♗g2 [25.♗xd6 ♘xh3#; 25.gxf4 ♖g6+–+] 25...♗xg2 26.♗xd6 ♗xd6 27.♖e1 [27.gxf4 ♗xf1 28.♔xf1 ♖xf4–+] 27...♘d3 28.♖e3 ♗c5! 29.♖ce2 [29.♖xd3 ♗e4 30.♖dd2 ♖xf2 31.♖xf2 ♗xc2–+] 29...♖xf2 0–1 [29...♖xf2 30.♖xf2 ♗xe3–+]

(157)

▷ V. Erdos
► H. Steingrimsson
European Team Championship
Crete, 28.10.2017

19.♖xd5! exd5 20.♕f5 ♗xc5 [20...♔g7 21.♘h5+ ♔h8 22.♘xf6 ♗xf6 23.♕xf6+ ♔h7 24.♕f5+ ♔g7 25.♕xd5 ♕e6 26.♕xc4 ♕xc4 27.♖xc4+–] 21.♕g4+ ♔h7 [21...♔h8 22.♕f4+–] 22.♘h5 ♖g8 23.♘xf6+ ♔h8 24.♕f5 1–0

(158)

▷ A. Rasmussen
► T. Nyback
European Team Championship
Crete, 30.10.2017

27.♘f5! gxf5 28.♕xf5 ♘f8 29.♗h6 ♘g6 [29...♕c7 30.e6 fxe6 31.♕g4++–] 30.♕xf7+! 1–0 [30.♕xf7+ ♔xf7 31.♗d5#]

(159)

▷ V. Kovalev
► D. Pavasovic
European Team Championship
Crete, 30.10.2017

20.♗d6!! ♗xb3 21.♗xf8 ♗d5 22.♗b4 +-

(160)

▷ A. Naiditsch
► N. Morozov
European Team Championsip Crete,
31.10.2017

21.♖a1! g5 [21...b4 22.axb4 ♕xb4 (22...♖ad8 23.♖ab1 ♕xc2 24.♖f2 ♖d3 25.♖xc2 ♖xe3 26.♔f2+-) 23.♖ab1+-; 21...♕xc2 22.♖fc1 ♕b3 23.♖cb1 ♕c2 24.♖a2+-] **22.♖a2 gxf4 23.♕e1** 1–0

(161)

▷ M. Bluebaum
► M. Bosiocic
European Team Championship
Crete, 01.11.2017

35...♗e6! 36.fxe3 ♗d8! 37.e4 ♗h3+ 38.♔f2 ♗h4+ −+

(162)

▷ G. Antal
► A. Adly
Tegernsee Open, 01.11.2017

27...♖xf4!! 28.♕e2 [28.♕xf4 ♗xa3+ 29.♔d1 (29.♖xa3 ♕e1#) 29...♖b1+ 30.♔e2 ♕e1+ 31.♔f3 ♕xf1+ 32.♔g3 (32.♔g4 h5+-+; 32.♔e4 d5+-+) 32...♕g1+ 33.♔f3 ♖f1+-+] **28...♖xh4 29.♖xh4 ♕xg5+ 30.♔e3 ♕xh4 31.♖b3 ♖xb3 32.cxb3 ♗xa3+** 0–1

(163)

▷ D. Howell
► J. Lopez Martinez
European Team Championship
Crete, 04.11.2017

75.g7? [75.f7! b2 76.♘c4 b1♕ 77.♘a3++-] **75...♖f5+?** [75...b2! 76.♘c4 (76.g8♕ b1♕ =) 76...♖c3!! 77.♘xb2 (77.g8♕ ♖f5+=) 77...♖f5+!! 78.♔d6 ♖xf6+ 79.♔e7 ♖g6=] **76.♔d4 b2 77.♘c4! ♖f4+ 78.♔e5 ♖xc4 79.g8♕ ♖c3 80.♕g2+ ♔b3 81.♕b7+ ♔c2 82.f7** +-

(164)

▷ D. Vocaturo
► Y. Pelletier
European Team Championship
Crete, 06.11.2017

26.♗xg6!! fxg6 27.♕xg6 ♖e7 [27...♖f8 28.♕h7+ ♔f7 29.♖g3 ♖g8 (29...♕f6 30.f5! exf5 31.♔f2! ♖h8 (31...♖ad8 32.♖eg1 ♖g8 33.♖g6+-) 32.♖xg7+ ♕xg7 33.♖e7+ ♕xe7 34.♕xg7++-) 30.f5! exf5 (30...♕f6 31.♖g6 ♕xf5 32.♖f1+-) 31.♕g6+ ♔f8 32.♖e5 a5 33.♖g5 ♕xg5+ (33...♖a6 34.♖exf5++-) 34.♕xg5 ♘e6 35.♖xf5++-] **28.♖e5 ♕e8 29.♕h7+ ♔f8 30.♖h6 ♖f7** [30...♕f7 31.♖g6 ♔e8 32.f5! ♔d7 33.fxe6+ ♘xe6 34.♕xf7 ♖xf7 35.♖exe6+-] **31.f5 ♕a4 32.♖e1** [32.b3+-] **32...♖xf5 33.♖g6 ♖f7 34.♕h8+ ♔e7 35.♕xa8 ♕b5 36.♕c8** 1–0

(165)

▷ F. Caruana
► A. Grischuk
Champions Showdown Saint Louis,
11.11.2017

20.♗xh6!! ♘xd4 [20...gxh6
21.♕e4+-] **21.♘xd4 gxh6** [21...cxd4
22.♕h5 g6 23.♕h3+-] **22.♕h5 ♗g5
23.h4 ♕xe5 24.hxg5 ♕xg5 25.♕xg5
hxg5 26.♘f3** +-

(166)

▷ B. Bogosavljevic
► N. Ostojic
Manojlovica Memoria Valjevo,
17.11.2017

18.♘xb6!! ♕xb6 **19.♕d4 ♖c8** [19...
♘fe4 20.f6 ♗xf6 21.♖xf6+ ♕xf6
22.♖f1+-] **20.♖ae1 ♖c6 21.♖f2**
♘fd7 [21...♘g8 22.f6! ♗xf6 23.♗xc5+
♔g7 24.♖e6 ♕xc5 25.♕d7+ ♘e7
26.♖exf6 ♖hf8 27.♕e6+-] **22.♗xc5+
♕xc5 23.♕xd7 ♕c7 24.♖e8+ ♖xe8
25.♕xc7** 1-0

(167)

▷ R. Li
► R. Prasanna
UT Dallas Fall Open, 18.11.2017

20.♗xh6! ♗xf5 [20...gxh6 21.♕xh6
♕g5 (21...♗xf5 22.exf5 f6 23.dxe5
dxe5 (23...fxe5 24.f6 ♕d7 25.♕h5+-;
23...♖xe5 24.♖xe5 dxe5 25.♗b3+♔h8
26.♕h5+-) 24.♖ad1 ♕e7 25.♗b3+
♔h8 26.♕h5+-) 22.♕xg5+ ♘xg5
23.♘f6+ ♔h8 24.♘xe8+-] **21.exf5**

e4 **22.♗xg7** 1-0 [22.♗xg7 ♔xg7
23.♕h6++-]

(168)

▷ G. Quparadze
► D. Paravyan
Gaprindashvili Cup Tbilisi,
19.11.2017

32.♖f1? [32.♕e8+! ♖f8 33.♕e4 g6
34.♕d5+ ♔g7 35.♘e6++-] **32...♕d7
33.♕xf7+ ♕xf7 34.♘xf7 a3 35.♗a1±**
0-1

(169)

▷ T. Luther
► G. Papp
Austrian League, 19.11.2017

**17...c4! 18.♕xb7 ♘c5 19.♖xd8 ♖axd8
20.♕b4 ♖d1+ 21.♘e1 ♘d3 22.♗d2**
[22.♕xc4+ ♔h8 23.♗d2 ♖xa1 24.g3
♘xe1 25.♗xe1 ♖xe1+-+] **22...♖xe1+**
0-1

(170)

▷ V. Belous
► A. Baryshpolets
American Open Costa Mesa,
25.11.2017

33.♘e3! ♖e2 [33...♖d2 34.♗xf6+-]
34.♔f3 [34.♔f1+-] **34...♗xd4
35.♔xe2 ♗c5 36.♔f3 b6 37.♘c4
g6 38.♘xb6** 1-0 [38.♘xb6 ♗xb6
39.♖d6+-]

[171]

▷ A. Horvath
► L. Gyorkos
Hungarian League, 26.11.2017

1.♘xe6! ♘xe6 2.♘d5 ♗xd5 3.exd5 ♘e5 [3...♘ec5 4.♕xe7 ♘xd3 5.♗h6+-] 4.dxe6 ♕c8 5.♗e3 ♗h4 6.e7 ♗xe7 7.♗xb6 ♖de8 8.♗e4±

[172]

▷ P. Acs
► J. Konnyu
Hungarian League, 26.11.2017

24.♘xf7! ♖xf7 [24...exd2 25.♘h6+ ♔h8 26.♕g8+ ♖xg8 27.♘f7#] 25.fxe3 ♗f6 [25...♖cc7 26.♗xc6 bxc6 27.♖xc6+-] 26.e4 ♕e7 27.♗b4 1-0

[173]

▷ Y. Shvayger
► E. Atalik
Holuj-Radzikowska Wroclaw, 30.11.2017

58.♖e6+! ♔f5 [58...♔d4 59.♖e7 ♕c4 60.♘e6+ ♔e3 (60...♔d5 61.♘gf4+ ♔e5 62.♖xf7+-) 61.♖xf7 ♕xe6 62.♖e7+-] 59.♔h3! 1-0 [59.♔h3 h5 (59...♕c3+ 60.g3+-) 60.♘e7+ ♔xf4 61.♘d5++-; 59.♘e7+? ♔g4 60.♖g6+ ♘g5 61.♘ed5 ♕e5 62.hxg5 hxg5=]

[174]

▷ M. Matlakov
► E. Inarkiev
Russian Championship St. Petersburg, 05.12.2017

31.♘dxe6? [31.♘xe4! ♕xc4 32.♘d6 ♕c7 33.♕xe6+ ♔h8 34.♕xd5+-] 31...♘xf2 [31...♕c6=] 32.♖d2 ♘h3+ 33.♔g2 ♕c6 34.♔xh3 ♖xd2 35.♕xd2+-

[175]

▷ L. Van Wely
► R. Kempinski
Bundesliga, 09.12.2017

15.♘xe6! fxe6 16.♕xg6+ ♔h8 17.♕xh6+ ♕h7 [17...♔g8 18.♕g6+ ♔h8 19.♘g5 ♗d5 20.♗xd5 exd5 21.♖h3+-] 18.♕xh7+ ♔xh7 19.♘g5+ ♗xg5 20.hxg5+ ♔g6 21.♗xe6 ♖h8 22.♖xh8 ♖xh8 23.♗h3±

[176]

▷ S. Volkov
► N. Vitiugov
Russian Championship St. Petersburg, 14.12.2017

14...♖xe3! 15.♗xg4 [15.♕xe3 ♗f4-+] 15...♖xc3+ 16.♕xc3 [16.bxc3 ♗f4-+] 16...♕g5+ 17.♔b1 ♕xg4 18.♘f3 ♘d7-+

(177)

▷ S. Lomasov
► N. Yakubboev
World Youth U16 Olympiad,
14.12.2017

23.♘e4! ♕f4 [23...dxe4 24.♖xg5++-; 23...♕e5 24.♖xg5+!+-] 24.♘f6+ ♔g7 25.♘e8+ ♔g6 26.♕g7+ 1–0 [26. ♕g7+ ♔xh5 27.♘f6++-]

(178)

▷ M. Kusiak
► M. Chigaev
European Championship Rapid Katowice, 16.12.2017

26...♖bd8! 0–1 [26...♖bd8 27.♖b1 ♕xg1 28.♖xg1 ♖d1+ 29.♖xd1 ♖xd1#]

(1)

▷ **D. Sadzikowski**
► **A. Mista**
Krakow Open, 02.01.2017

1...–+

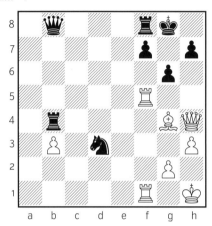

(2)

▷ **D. Naroditsky**
► **K. Priyadharshan**
Internet Pro League Rapid, 11.01.2017

1.+-

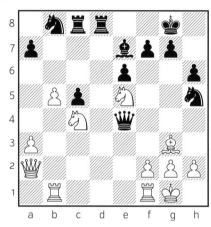

(3)

▷ **H. Tikkanen**
► **T. Hillarp Persson**
Swedish League, 14.01.2017

1.+-

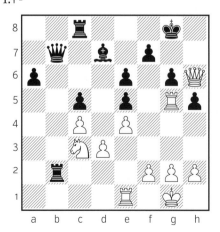

(4)

▷ **W. So**
► **R. Rapport**
Wijk aan Zee, 16.01.2017

1...–+

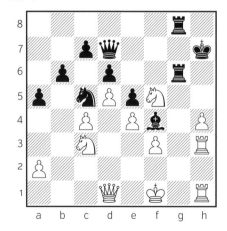

(5)

▷ **M. Ragger**
► **E. Hansen**
Wijk aan Zee, 16.01.2017

1.+-

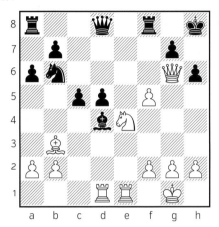

(6)

▷ **B. Adhiban**
► **D. Andreikin**
Wijk aan Zee, 22.01.2017

1.+-

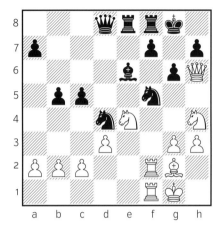

(7)

▷ **M. Gagunashvili**
► **D. Jojua**
Georgian Championship, 23.01.2017

1...−+

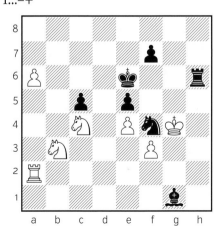

(8)

▷ **L. Aronian**
► **R. Rapport**
Wijk aan Zee, 25.01.2017

1.+-

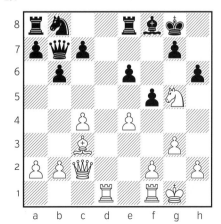

(9)

▷ **B. Jobava**
▶ **J. Lopez Martinez**
Catalan League, 28.01.2017

1.+−

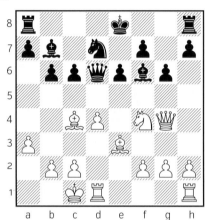

(10)

▷ **A. Huzman**
▶ **D. Howell**
Gibraltar Masters, 31.01.2017

1...−+

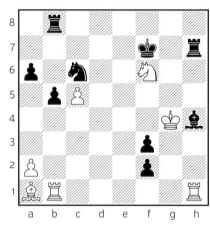

(11)

▷ **M. Cornette**
▶ **A. Stukopin**
Internet Pro League Rapid, 11.02.2017

1...−+

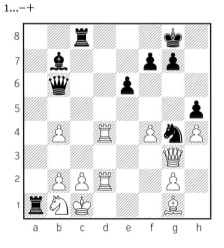

(12)

▷ **L. Ding**
▶ **R. Rapport**
Sharjah Fide GP, 18.02.2017

1...−+

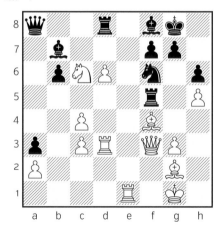

(13)

▷ **M. Bluebaum**
► **M. Pavlovic**
Aeroflot Open Moscow, 21.02.2017

1...=

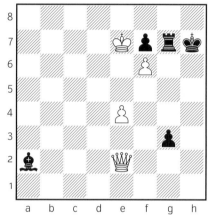

(14)

▷ **M. Pavlovic**
► **B. Lalith**
Aeroflot Open Moscow, 22.02.2017

1...−+

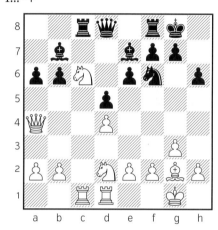

(15)

▷ **K. Dragun**
► **I. Nyzhnyk**
Internet Pro League Rapid, 22.02.2017

1...−+

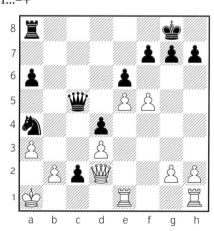

(16)

▷ **S. Vidit**
► **F. Bindrich**
Aeroflot Open Moscow, 01.03.2017

1.+−

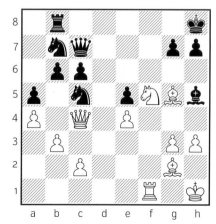

(17)

▷ **J. Glud**
► **V. Laznicka**
Jurmala Tal Memorial R, 04.03.2017

1...−+

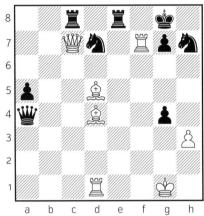

(18)

▷ **A. Shirov**
► **K. Kulaots**
Finnish League, 12.03.2017

1.+−

(19)

▷ **Y. Wei**
► **Y. Xu**
HD Bank Open, 16.03.2017

1.+−

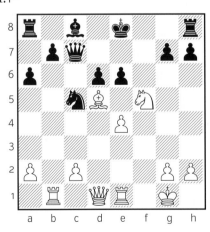

(20)

▷ **R. Li**
► **Y. Zherebukh**
Saint Louis Winter-A, 16.03.2017

1...−+

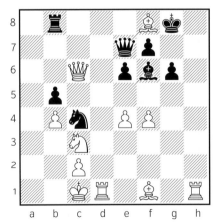

(21)

▷ **V. Fedoseev**
► **S. Shankland**
Saint Louis Winter-A, 19.03.2017

1.-/+

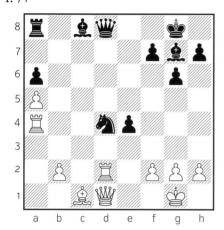

(22)

▷ **J. Xiong**
► **A. Shabalov**
USA Championship, 05.04.2017

1...−+

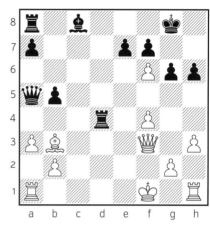

(23)

▷ **J. Xiong**
► **W. So**
USA Championship, 07.04.2017

1...−+

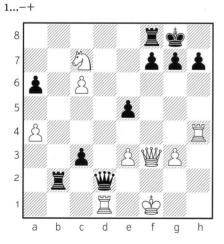

(24)

▷ **J. Ramiro Overejo**
► **F. Peralta**
La Roda Open, 14.04.2017

1...−+

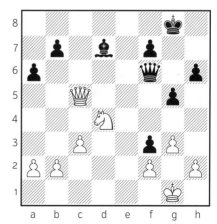

(25)

▷ **H. Nakamura**
▶ **G. Oparin**
Chess Challenge Blitz, 17.04.2017

1. +/-

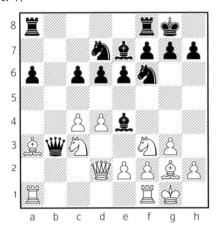

(26)

▷ **S. Martinovic**
▶ **A. Saric**
Croatian Championship, 28.04.2017

1.+-

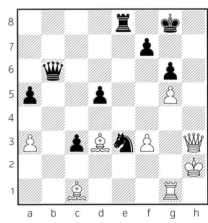

(27)

▷ **E. Najer**
▶ **S. Mamedyarov**
Russian League, 05.05.2017

1...−+

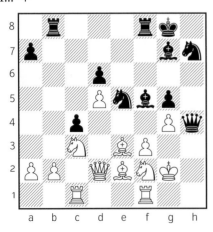

(28)

▷ **I. Nepomniachtchi**
▶ **S. Salem**
Fide GP Moscow, 14.05.2017

1...−+

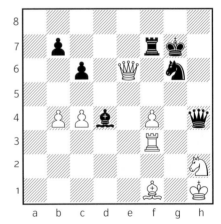

(29)

▷ **M. Tabatabaei**
▶ **Y. Wang**
Asian Continental Open, 19.05.2017

1.+-

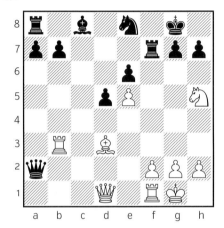

(30)

▷ **K. Piorun**
▶ **J. Degraeve**
French League, 19.05.2017

1...−+

(31)

▷ **P. Tworzydlo**
▶ **M. Kanarek**
Katowice Rapid, 20.05.2017

1...−+

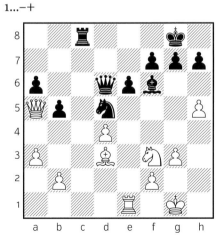

(32)

▷ **C. Li**
▶ **A. Neiksans**
French League, 21.05.2017

1.+-

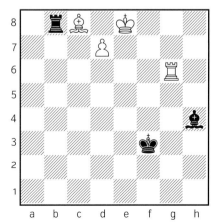

(33)

▷ A. Naiditsch
► N. Brunner

French League, 22.05.2017

1.+-

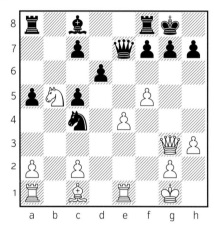

(34)

▷ A. Alonso Rosell
► I. Kovalenko

European Championship, 31.05.2017

1.+-

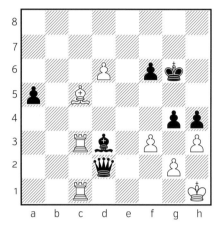

(35)

▷ B. Dastan
► R. Edouard

European Championship, 01.06.2017

1.+-

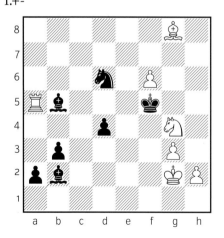

(36)

▷ G. Froewis
► R. Svane

European Championship, 03.06.2017

1...−+

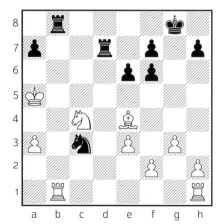

(37)

▷ I. Ivanisevic
► D. Bocharov
European Championship, 06.06.2017

1.+-

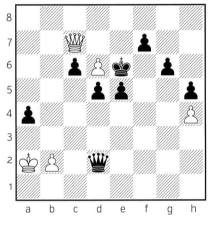

(38)

▷ V. Moiseenko
► N. Maiorov
Nezhmetdinov Memorial, 07.06.2017

1.+-

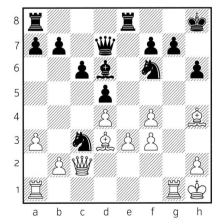

(39)

▷ V. Usmanov
► B. Macieja
European Championship, 09.06.2017

1.+-

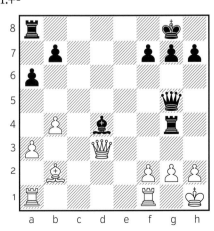

(40)

▷ A. Gorovets
► D. Asaria
Las Vegas National Open, 17.06.2017

1.+-

(41)

▷ **D. Flores**
▶ **A. Kovalyov**
American Continental, 17.06.2017

1.+−

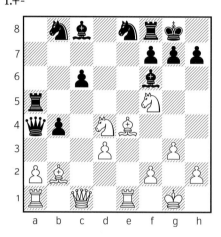

(42)

▷ **F. Caruana**
▶ **W. So**
Paris GCT Rapid, 21.06.2017

1. +/−

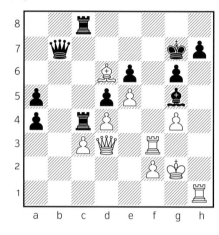

(43)

▷ **D. Arutinian**
▶ **A. Zubov**
Asrian Memorial Yerevan, 24.06.2017

1...−+

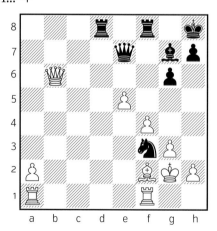

(44)

▷ **T. Burg**
▶ **B. Bok**
Dutch Championship, 01.07.2017

1...−+

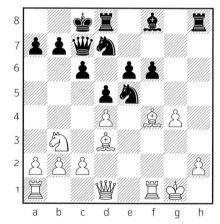

(45)

▷ **P. Ponkratov**
► **E. Najer**
Russian Higher League, 10.07.2017

1...−+

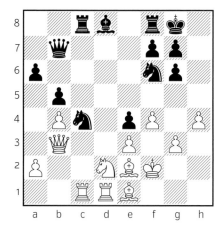

(46)

▷ **R. Barski**
► **B. Heberla**
Najdorf Memorial, 11.07.2017

1.+−

(47)

▷ **Q. Ma**
► **Q. Liu**
Chinese League, 28.07.2017

1.+−

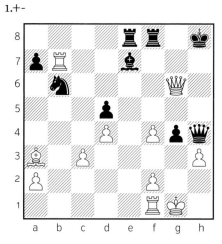

(48)

▷ **R. Vaganian**
► **Y. Hou**
Biel GM, 01.08.2017

1...−/+

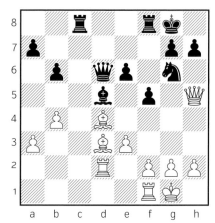

(49)

▷ Y. Zinchenko
► D. Balokas
Heraklion Gazi Open, 05.08.2017

1. +/-

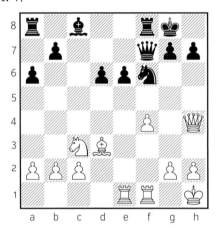

(50)

▷ V. Anand
► F. Caruana
Sinquefield Cup, 06.08.2017

1.+-

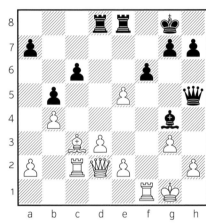

(51)

▷ H. Nakamura
► L. Aronian
Sinquefield Cup, 09.08.2017

1...−+

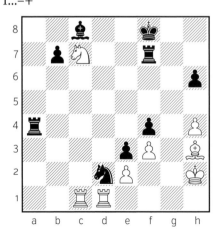

(52)

▷ L. Ding
► A. Giri
Wenzhou, 09.08.2017

1...−+

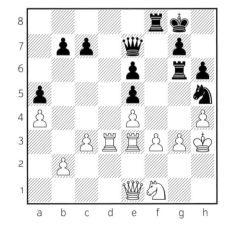

(53)

▷ **S. Mareco**
▶ **S. Ganguly**
Spanish League, 15.08.2017

1...−+

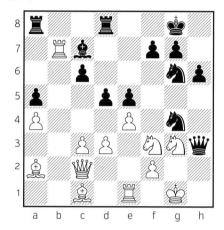

(54)

▷ **J. Friedel**
▶ **F. Libiszewski**
Washington Open, 15.08.2017

1.+−

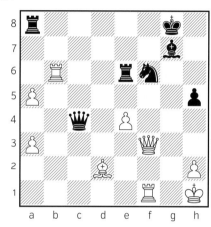

(55)

▷ **Q. Le**
▶ **D. Navara**
Saint Louis Rapid, 16.08.2017

1.+−

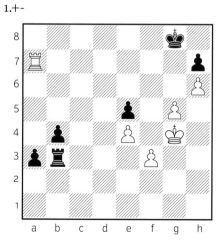

(56)

▷ **H. Wang**
▶ **X. Bu**
Chinese League, 20.08.2017

1... −/+

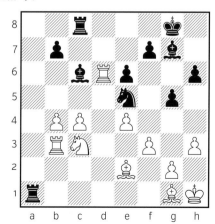

(57)

▷ **A. Strikovic**
► **V. Sanal**
Serbian League, 01.09.2017

1...−+

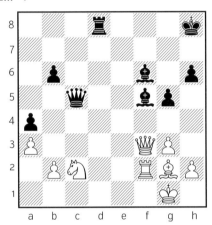

(58)

▷ **B. Jobava**
► **Y. Yu**
Fide World Cup Tbilisi, 08.09.2017

1. +/-

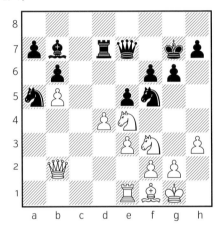

(59)

▷ **M. Matlakov**
► **L. Aronian**
Fide World Cup Tbilisi, 10.09.2017

1.+-

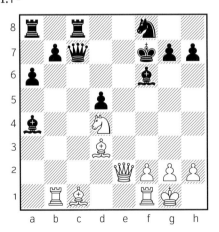

(60)

▷ **J. Moussard**
► **D. Fridman**
Paris Oscaro Blitz, 16.09.2017

1.+-

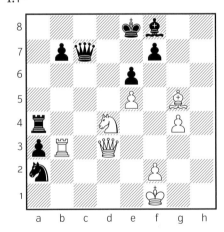

(61)

▷ **D. Naroditsky**
► **S. Shankland**
Imre Konig Memorial R, 17.09.2017

1.+-

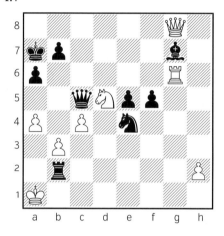

(62)

▷ **E. Perelshteyn**
► **D. Howell**
Douglas IoM Open, 29.09.2017

1...–+

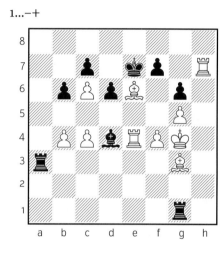

(63)

▷ **V. Malakhov**
► **B. Predojevic**
Croatian League, 01.10.2017

1.+-

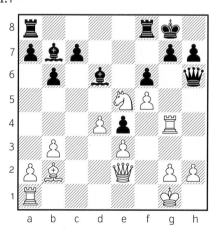

(64)

▷ **B. Savchenko**
► **D. Andreikin**
Russian Champ. Blitz, 02.10.2017

1. +/-

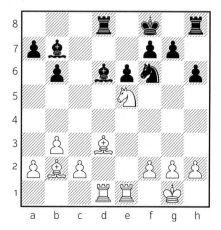

(65)

▷ **G. Sargissian**
► **S. Bogner**
European Team Champ., 28.10.2017

1. +/-

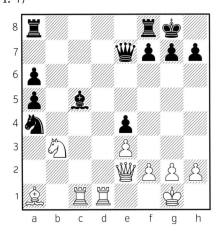

(66)

▷ **M. Tabatabaei**
► **G. Sibashvili**
Teheran Paytakht Cup, 30.10.2017

1.+-

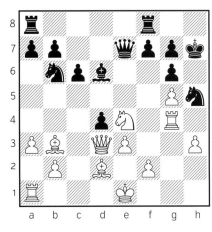

(67)

▷ **J. Bai**
► **L. Ding**
Chinese League, 04.11.2017

1...−+

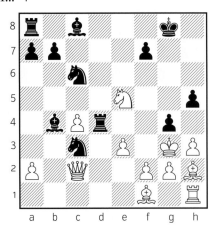

(68)

▷ **R. Rapport**
► **D. Howell**
European Team Champ., 06.11.2017

1.+-

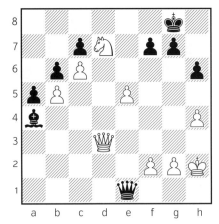

(69)

▷ **H. Asis Gargatagli**
▶ **A. Alonso Rosell**
Barcelona GM, 09.11.2017

1.+-

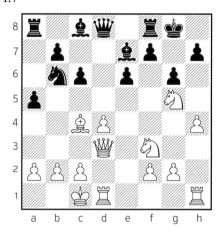

(70)

▷ **P. Ponkratov**
▶ **A. Goganov**
Ugra Governor's Cup Blitz, 23.11.2017

1.+-

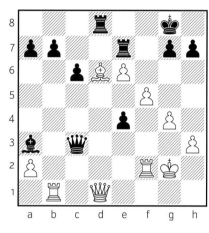

(71)

▷ **D. Howell**
▶ **L. McShane**
British KO Championship, 09.12.2017

1...−+

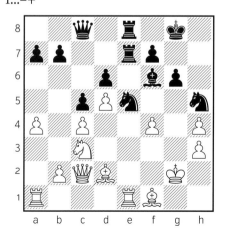

(72)

▷ **V. Plat**
▶ **K. Szadkowski**
European Champ. Rapid, 16.12.2017

1.+-

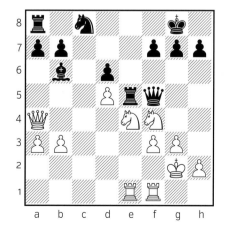

– SOLUTIONS –

(1)

▷ D. Sadzikowski
▶ A. Mista
Krakow Open, 02.01.2017

43...♘f4! 44.♕g5 [44.♖f6 ♘h5
45.♖6f3 f5 46.♕f2 ♘g7–+; 44.♖c5 h5
45.♗f3 ♘e2–+] 44...♘e6 45.♕h6
♖xg4 46.hxg4 gxf5 47.gxf5 ♘g7
48.f6 ♘e6 49.♕h4 ♖d8 50.♖e1
♖d4 51.♕f2 ♕f4 0–1

(2)

▷ D. Naroditsky
▶ K. Priyadharshan
Internet Pro League Rapid, 11.01.2017

22.♘xf7! ♔xf7 23.♘e5+ ♔f6 [23...
♔g8 24.♕xe6+ ♔h7 25.♖be1+–]
24.♖be1! ♕f5 [24...♕d5 25.♕c2+–]
25.♗h4+ g5 26.g4! ♕f4 [26...♕h7
27.f4! gxh4 28.f5+–] 27.♗g3 ♕d2
28.♕b1! ♖g8 29.♕h7 1–0

(3)

▷ H. Tikkanen
▶ T. Hillarp Persson
Swedish League, 14.01.2017

25.h4!! ♗e8 26.♖xh5! 1–0[26.♖xh5
gxh5 27.♖e3+–]

(4)

▷ W. So
▶ R. Rapport
Wijk aan Zee, 16.01.2017

31...b5!! [31...♖g2 32.♘e2!] 32.cxb5
[32.♘xb5 ♖g2 33.h5 ♖d2–+; 32.h5 ♖g2
33.♘e2 bxc4–+] 32...♖g2! 33.♕b1
[33.♘e2 ♕xb5–+] 33...♕f7? [33...
♖d2! 34.♘e2 (34.♖g1 ♖xg1+ 35.♔xg1
♕e8–+) 34...♘d3 35.a4 c6! 36.dxc6
♕a7 37.b6 ♕xb6 38.♕xb6 ♖d1#; 33...
c6! 34.dxc6 ♕a7 35.b6 ♕a6+ 36.♕b5
♕xb5+ 37.♘xb5 ♘d3–+] 34.♘e2
♕g6?? 35.♘e7 +–

(5)

▷ M. Ragger
▶ E. Hansen
Wijk aan Zee, 16.01.2017

21.f6! ♕c7 [21...♗xf6 22.♘d6! ♕xd6
23.♗c2+–] 22.♘g5! gxf6 23.♕xh6+
♔g8 24.♘e6 1–0

(6)

▷ B. Adhiban
▶ D. Andreikin
Wijk aan Zee, 22.01.2017

21.♖xf5!! [21.♘xf5 ♘xf5 22.♖xf5
♗xf5 23.♖xf5 ♖xe4!] 21...♘xf5 [21...
♗xf5 22.♘g5+–] 22.♖xf5! ♕d4+
[22...gxf5 23.♘f6++–; 22...♗xf5
23.♘xf5 gxf5 24.♘f6++–] 23.♖f2 f5
24.♘g5 [24.♘xg6!? hxg6 25.♕xg6+
♕g7 26.♘f6+ ♖xf6 27.♕xe8++–] 24...
♕g7 25.♕xg7+ ♔xg7 26.♗c6+–

(7)

▷ M. Gagunashvili
► D. Jojua
Georgian Championship, 23.01.2017

63...♖g6+! 64.♔h4 f5! 65.exf5+ [65.a7 ♖h6+ 66.♔g3 (*66.♔g5 ♖h5#*) 66...♖h3#] **65...♔xf5 66.♘xe5 ♖h6+** 0–1[66...♖h6+ 67.♔g3 ♖h3#]

(8)

▷ L. Aronian
► R. Rapport
Wijk aan Zee, 25.01.2017

19.exf5!! hxg5 [19...exf5 20.♖fe1! ♖xe1+ (*20...♘a6 21.♘e6+-*) 21.♖xe1 hxg5 22.♕xf5 c6 23.♖e8 ♕f7 24.♕c8+-] **20.f6! c5** [20...c6 21.f4 g4 22.fxg7 ♗c5+ (*22...♗xg7 23.♕g6 ♕f7 24.♕xg4+-*) 23.♔h1 ♗b4 24.f5 ♗xc3 25.f6+-] **21.f4! g4 22.f5 gxf6 23.fxe6 ♕h7 24.♕g2! ♘a6 25.♖d7 ♕h5 26.♖xf6 ♖ad8 27.♖xf8+! ♔xf8 28.♕f1+** 1–0

(9)

▷ B. Jobava
► J. Lopez Martinez
Catalan League, 28.01.2017

15.♘xe6! fxe6 16.♗f4! ♕e7 [16... ♕f8 17.♖he1 0-0-0 18.♖xe6+-] **17.♖he1 0-0-0** [17...♘f8 18.♗xe6+-] **18.♖xe6 ♕f8 19.♖xc6+!!** 1–0[19. ♖xc6+ ♗xc6 20.♗a6+ ♗b7 21.♕f3! ♗xa6 22.♕c6#]

(10)

▷ A. Huzman
► D. Howell
Gibraltar Masters, 31.01.2017

41...♖g7+! 42.♔xh4 [42.♔f5 ♘e7+ 43.♔e4 ♗xf6-+] **42...♘e7!! 43.♘h5 ♘f5+ 44.♔h3 ♖g5 45.♖hd1 ♖bg8 46.♖d7+ ♔e6 47.♖h7 ♖xh5+** 0–1[47...♖xh5+ 48.♖xh5 ♖g1-+]

(11)

▷ M. Cornette
► A. Stukopin
Internet Pro League R, 11.02.2017

24... ♗d5! 25.♖xd5 [25.b3 ♕a7 26.c4 ♕a3+ 27.♖b2 ♗xc4-+] **25...♕xg1+ 26.♖d1 ♘e3! 27.♖d8+** [27.♖xg1 ♖xc2#] **27...♔h7! 28.c3 ♘xd1** -+

(12)

▷ L. Ding
► R. Rapport
Sharjah Fide GP, 18.02.2017

34...♖xd6! 35.♖xd6 [35.♗xd6 ♖xf3 36.♗xf3 ♗xc6-+] **35...♗xd6 36.♘e7+ ♗xe7 37.♕xb7 ♗c5+! 38.♔f1** [38.♔h1 ♖xh5+-+; 38.♗e3 ♕xb7 39.♗xb7 ♖e5-+] **38...♕xb7 39.♗xb7 ♘xh5 40.♖e8+ ♗f8** 0–1

(13)

▷ M. Bluebaum
► M. Pavlovic
Aeroflot Open Moscow, 21.02.2017

71...♖g5? [71...♖g6! 72.♕xa2 g2 73.♕xf7+ ♔h6 74.♕f8+ ♔g5=] **72.♕xa2 g2 73.♕xf7+ ♔h6 74.♕f8+ ♔h7 75.♕f7+ ♔h8** [75...♔h6 76.♕e6 g1♕ 77.f7+ ♔h5 78.♕h3+ ♔g6 79.f8N+ ♔g7 80.♕h7#] **76.♕e6 g1♕ 77.♕h3+** 1–0

(14)

▷ M. Pavlovic
► B. Lalith
Aeroflot Open Moscow, 22.02.2017

16...♗xc6! 17.♖xc6 ♕d7 18.♖dc1 ♗c5! 19.R1xc5 bxc5 –+

(15)

▷ K. Dragun
► I. Nyzhnyk
Internet Pro League R, 22.02.2017

25...♘xb2! 26.♔xb2 [26.♕b4 ♕xb4 27.axb4 ♘xd3–+] **26...♖b8+ 27.♔a2 ♕d5+! 28.♔a1 ♕b3 29.♕c1 ♕c3+ 30.♔a2 ♕xd3 31.fxe6 fxe6 32.♖hf1 ♕b3+ 33.♔a1 ♕c3+ 34.♔a2 d3** 0–1[34...d3 35.♖f2 ♕c4+ 36.♔a1 ♕d4+ 37.♔a2 ♕xf2–+]

(16)

▷ S. Vidit
► F. Bindrich
Aeroflot Open Moscow, 01.03.2017

32.♘xg7! ♘d6 [32...♕xg7 33.♗f6+–; 32...♔xg7 33.♗f6+ ♔g6 (*33...♔h6 34.♕c3+–*) 34.g4 ♗xg4 35.♗xe5! ♕xe5 36.♕f7+ ♔g5 37.hxg4 ♔xg4

38.♖f5+–] **33.♘e8!! ♗f7** [33...♘xe8 34.♖f8+ ♔g7 35.♕g8#] **34.♘xc7 ♗xc4 35.bxc4 ♖c8 36.♗f6+ ♔g8 37.♗xe5 ♘xc4 38.♗f4 ♘xa4 39.h4** 1–0

(17)

▷ J. Glud
► V. Laznicka
Jurmala Tal Memorial R, 04.03.2017

38...♕xd1+?? [38...♘hf6!! 39.♖xd7+ **a)** 39.♖xf6+ ♔h7–+; **b)** 39.♖f8+ ♔h7!–+; **c)** 39.♖e7+ ♘xd5 40.♖xg7+ ♔h8 41.♖xd7+ ♕xd4+ 42.♖xd4 ♘xc7–+; **d)** 39.♖xg7+ ♔h8!–+ (*39...♔xg7 40.♗xf6+ ♔xf6–+*) ; 39...♔h8!–+; 38...♕xd4+ 39.♖xd4 ♖xc7 40.♖xd7++–] **39.♖f1+ ♔h8 40.♗xg7+! ♔xg7 41.♕xd7+ ♔h6 42.♖xd1** +–

(18)

▷ A. Shirov
► K. Kulaots
Finnish League, 12.03.2017

24.gxh7! ♖xe3 25.♖g1+ ♔h8 [25...♖xh7 26.fxe3+–] **26.fxe3 ♘f5 27.♖g8+ ♔xh7 28.♖h2+ ♘h6 29.♖g1** 1–0

(19)

▷ Y. Wei
► Y. Xu
HD Bank Open, 16.03.2017

18.♗c6+!! ♕xc6 [18...bxc6 19.♘xd6+ ♔e7 20.♕g4! ♕xd6 (*20...♖g8*

21.♕g5+ ♔d7 22.♖ed1+-) 21.♕xg7+
♔e8 22.♕xh8+ ♕f8 23.♕xh7+-;
*18...♔d8 19.♘xd6 ♕xc6 20.♘f7+
♔c7 21.♘xh8+-]* **19.♘xd6+ ♔e7
20.♕g4! ♘d7** *[20...♔xd6 21.♖ed1+
♔c7 22.♕g3++-]* **21.e5** 1-0

(20)

▷ **R. Li**
► **Y. Zherebukh**
Saint Louis Winter-A, 16.03.2017

26...♕a7!! 27.♗xc4 *[27.♖d3 ♕a1+
28.♘b1 ♗b2+ 29.♔d1 ♕xb1+ 30.♔e2
♕xc2+ 31.♔f3 ♘e5+ 32.fxe5 ♕xc6-+]*
**27...♗xc3 28.♖h8+ ♔xh8 29.♖h1+
♔g8 30.♗a2** *[30.♔d1 ♕e3 31.♕d6
♕f3+ 32.♔c1 ♕xh1+ 33.♕d1 ♖a8-+]*
**30...♕a3+ 31.♔d1 ♖d8+ 32.♔e2
♖d2+ 33.♔f3 ♖xc2! 34.♔g4
♖g2+ 35.♔h3 ♗e1+** 0-1*[35...♗e1+
36.♔xg2 ♕g3+ 37.♔f1 ♕f2#]*

(21)

▷ **V. Fedoseev**
► **S. Shankland**
Saint Louis Winter-A, 19.03.2017

22...♘f3+! 23.gxf3 ♕g5+ 24.♔h1
[24.♔f1 ♗h3+ 25.♔e1 e3-+] **24...
♗h3 25.♕g1 ♕h5 26.♕d1** *[26.♕g3
♕b5 27.♖xh3 ♕xa4 28.fxe4 ♕xe4+∓;
26.♖a3 ♗f8µ]* **26...♗e5 27.♖a3** *[27.
♖xe4 ♗g4!-+]* **27...♗g4 28.♕g1
♗xf3+ 29.♖xf3 ♕xf3+ 30.♕g2
♖c8 31.♕xf3 exf3 32.♖d1 ♖c2** -+

(22)

▷ **J. Xiong**
► **A. Shabalov**
USA Championship, 05.04.2017

21...♕b6! 22.f5 *[22.♕xa8 ♖xf4+
23.♔e2 ♖f2+ 24.♔d3 ♔h7!! 25.♕xc8
♕d6+ 26.♔c3 ♕d2#; 22.♖e1 b4!
23.♖xe7 (23.♕xa8 ♖xf4+ 24.♔e2
♖f2+ 25.♔d3 ♕d6+ 26.♗d5 ♔h7!!
27.♕c6 ♗a6+ 28.♔d4 ♕f4+ 29.♖e4
♖d2+ 30.♔c5 ♖c2+-+) 23...♗a6+
24.♔e1 ♖f8-+]* **22...♗b7 23.♕g3 g5
24.fxe7 ♖e8 25.♖e1 ♖f4+ 26.♔e2
♕d4** 0-1

(23)

▷ **J. Xiong**
► **W. So**
USA Championship, 07.04.2017

28...♖d8! 29.♘d5 *[29.♖xd2 ♖dxd2
30.♔g1 ♖b1+ 31.♕f1 c2 32.♖c4 ♖dd1
33.♖xc2 ♖xf1+ 34.♔g2 ♖fc1-+]* **29...
♖xd5 30.♖d4 ♖xd4** *[30...exd4??
31.c7+-]* **31.exd4 ♕xd1+** 0-1*[31...
♕xd1+ 32.♕xd1 c2 33.♕c1 ♖b1 34.c7
♖xc1+ 35.♔e2 ♖e1+ 36.♔xe1 c1♕+-+]*

(24)

▷ **J. Ramiro Overejo**
► **F. Peralta**
La Roda Open, 14.04.2017

**24...♕g6! 25.♘xf3 ♕b1+ 26.♔g2
♗c6 27.h3 ♕e4 28.♕e3 f5 29.g4
f4** 0-1

(25)

▷ H. Nakamura
► G. Oparin
Chess Challenge Blitz, 17.04.2017

16.♘e5! dxe5 [16...♗xg2 17.♖fb1 ♕xa3 18.♘xd7 ♕xa1 19.♘xf6+ ♗xf6 20.♖xa1 ♗h3±; 16...♘xe5 17.dxe5 ♗xg2 18.♔xg2±] **17.♗xe7 exd4** [17... ♗xg2 18.♖fb1 ♕xc4 19.♗b4 ♕xb4 20.♗xb4 c5 21.♗xc5 ♘xc5 22.dxc5 ♗c6±] **18.♘xe4 ♘xe4 19.♗xe4 ♖fe8 20.♗xc6 ♖a7 21.♕xd4** 1–0

(26)

▷ S. Martinovic
► A. Saric
Croatian Championship, 28.04.2017

41.♖h1!! ♕d4 [41...♔f8 42.♔g3+-] **42.♔g3 ♖e6 43.♗xe3** 1–0[43.♗xe3 ♖xe3 44.♕c8++-]

(27)

▷ E. Najer
► S. Mamedyarov
Russian League, 05.05.2017

23...♘xf3!! 24.♗xf3 [24.♔xf3 ♗e4+ 25.♔xe4 ♖be8#] **24...♗e5! 25.♖h1** [25.♖g1 ♗d3 26.♗e2 (26. ♘xd3 cxd3-+) 26...♕h2+ 27.♔f1 ♕h3+ 28.♔e1 (28.♖g2 ♗xc3 29.♕xc3 ♗e4-+) 28...♖xf2 29.♗xf2 ♗f4 30.♕d1 ♖xb2-+] **25...♕g3+ 26.♔f1 ♗d3+ 27.♗e2 ♖xb2!! 28.♕xb2 ♕xe3 29.♗xd3** [29.♘cd1 ♖xf2+ 30.♘xf2 ♗xb2-+] **29...cxd3 30.♖c2** [30.♖e1 ♕f3 31.♖h6 ♗d4 32.♖h2 ♗xf2 33.♕xf2 d2-+] **30...dxc2**

31.♕xc2 ♖xf2+ 32.♔xf2 ♕xc3 33.♔g2 ♕c4 0–1

(28)

▷ I. Nepomniachtchi
► S. Salem
Fide GP Moscow, 14.05.2017

46...♘e5!! 47.♖h3 [47.fxe5 ♖xf3-+] **47...♕xf4 48.♕e8 ♕e4+ 49.♘f3 ♖xf3 50.♕h8+ ♔f7 51.♖h7+ ♔e6 52.♕c8+ ♔f6 53.♕f8+ ♔g5 54.♕h6+ ♔f5 55.♕f8+** [55.♕h5+ ♔f6 56.♖h6+ ♔e7-+] **55...♔g4** 0–1

(29)

▷ M. Tabatabaei
► Y. Wang
Asian Continental Open, 19.05.2017

19.♗b1! ♕a5 20.♖h3 g6 21.♕g4 ♔f8 22.♗xg6 hxg6 23.♕xg6 ♔e7 24.♘f6 1–0[24.♘f6 ♘xf6 (24...♗d7 25.♖h7+-) 25.exf6+ ♖xf6 26.♖h7++-]

(30)

▷ K. Piorun
► J. Degraeve
French League, 19.05.2017

15...g5! 16.♖c7 ♖ac8! 17.♕xb7 [17. ♖xd7 ♖xc1+ 18.♗f1 gxf4-+; 17.♖xc8 ♖xc8 18.♖xc8+ ♕xc8-+] **17... gxf4 18.♕xa7 ♖xc7** [18...♘e8!-+] **19.♖xc7 ♕b5** -+

(31)

▷ P. Tworzydlo
▶ M. Kanarek
Katowice Rapid, 20.05.2017

25...♖c3!! 26.♗xb5 [26.bxc3 ♗d8-+]
26...♖xf3 27.♗xa6 ♗xd4 0-1

(32)

▷ C. Li
▶ A. Neiksans
French League, 21.05.2017

98.♖g4!! [98.♖h6 ♖b4 99.♖xh4
♖xh4 100.d8♕ ♖h8+=] **98...♗f6**
[98...♔xg4 99.d8♕++-] **99.♖g7!!**
♖b4 100.♖f7! ♖e4+ 101.♔f8 ♖f4
102.♖xf6 ♖xf6+ 103.♔e7 1-0

(33)

▷ A. Naiditsch
▶ N. Brunner
French League, 22.05.2017

19.♘xc7!! ♕xc7 20.f6 g6 21.♕g5
♔h8 22.♖f1 d5 [22...♘e5 23.♖f4
♗g4 24.hxg4 ♖g8 25.♔f2+-] **23.♖f4**
♕e5 24.♕h6 ♕d4+ 25.♔h2 1-0[25.
♔h2 ♖g8 26.♕xh7+ ♔xh7 27.♖h4#]

(34)

▷ A. Alonso Rosell
▶ I. Kovalenko
European Championship, 31.05.2017

46.♖xd3? [46.♗e3!! ♕xe3 47.♖d1
gxh3 (47...gxf3 48.♖cxd3 fxg2+
49.♔xg2 ♕e2+ 50.♔g1+-) 48.♖cxd3

hxg2+ 49.♔xg2 ♕e2+ 50.♔h1
h3 51.♖1d2 ♕e1+ 52.♔h2 ♕e5+
53.♔xh3+-] **46...♕xc1+ 47.♗g1**
gxh3 48.♖d4 ♕f1 49.♖g4+ ♔h5-+

(35)

▷ B. Dastan
▶ R. Edouard
European Championship, 01.06.2017

52.f7! ♘xf7 53.♗xf7 ♔e4 [53...a1♕
54.♖xb5+ ♔g4 (54...♔e4 55.♗g6#)
55.h3#] **54.♖xb5 ♔d3** [54...a1♕
55.♗g6#] **55.♖xb3+ ♔c3 56.♖a3**
a1♕ 57.♖xa1 ♗xa1 58.♗g6+ 1-0

(36)

▷ G. Froewis
▶ R. Svane
European Championship, 03.06.2017

23...♖c8! 24.♖hc1 [24.♖b4 ♘xe4
25.♖c1 ♖d5+ 26.♖b5 ♘d2-+] **24...**
♖xc4 25.♖b4 ♖c5+ 26.♔a6 ♘xe4
0-1

(37)

▷ I. Ivanisevic
▶ D. Bocharov
European Championship, 06.06.2017

41.♕e7+! [41.d7? ♕c2 42.d8♕ ♕b3+
43.♔b1 ♕d1+=] **41...♔f5 42.d7 ♕d3**
43.♕xf7+ ♔g4 44.♕e6+ ♔f4
45.♕xc6 ♕b3+ 46.♔b1 1-0[46.
♔b1 ♕d1+ (46...♕d3+ 47.♕c2+-)
47.♕c1++-]

[38]

▷ V. Moiseenko
▶ N. Maiorov
Nezhmetdinov Memorial, 07.06.2017

30.♘e5!! ♕xe5 31.♕xd3! ♕b2+
[31...♖xe1 32.♕d8+ ♔f7 33.c5++-]
32.♖f2 [32.♕c2 ♕xc2+ 33.♗xc2 ♖xe1
34.♖xe1+-] **32...♕xf2+ 33.♔xf2**
♖xd3 34.e8♕+ ♘xe8 35.♖xe8+
♔f7 36.♖a8 ♗b7 37.♖a7 +-

[39]

▷ V. Usmanov
▶ B. Macieja
European Championship, 09.06.2017

23.f4! [23.♗xd4? ♕d5=] **23...♕d5**
[23...♖xf4 24.♗xd4+-] **24.♖f3 ♖d8
25.♖d1 ♕a2 26.♖f2 ♖g6 27.♗xd4
♕d5 28.♖fd2 ♖gd6 29.♕g3 ♖g6
30.♗e3** 1–0

[40]

▷ A. Gorovets
▶ D. Asaria
Las Vegas National Open, 17.06.2017

**20.♗xf6! gxf6 21.♗f5 ♕e7
22.♕f2!! ♘d1** [22...♕xe3 23.♕h4
♕xf3+ 24.♖g2+-] **23.♕h4! ♘f2+
24.♔xf2 ♕f8 25.♕h4 ♗e7 26.♖g3
♗d8 27.♖ag1 ♖xe3 28.♖g8+** 1–0

[41]

▷ D. Flores
▶ A. Kovalyov
American Continental, 17.06.2017

21.♘h6+! ♔h8 [21...gxh6
22.♕xh6+-] **22.♘xf7+ ♔g8** [22...
♖xf7 23.♗xc6 ♘xc6 24.♖xe8+ ♖f8
25.♖xf8#] **23.♕c4 ♖d5 24.♗xd5
cxd5 25.♕xc8 ♘d6 26.♕xf8+
♔xf8 27.♘xd6** 1–0

[42]

▷ F. Caruana
▶ W. So
Paris GCT Rapid, 21.06.2017

31.♖f6!! ♗xf6 [31...♖xc3
32.♖xh7++-; 31...♖g8 32.♕f3+-]
32.exf6+ ♔g8 [32...♗xf6
33.♗e5++-] **33.♗e7! ♖4c7** [33...♖f8
34.♗xf8 ♔xf8 35.♖b1 ♕d7 36.♕h3
♖c8 37.♖b6+-] **34.♗d6?** [34.f7+!+-
♔g7 (34...♔xf7 35.♖xh7++-) 35.♕e3
♖xe7 36.♕e5+ ♔xf7 37.♖xh7+ ♔e8
38.♕h8+ ♔d7 39.♖xe7+ ♔c6 40.♕g7
♖c7 41.♖xe6+ ♔b5 42.♕xg6 ♖xc3
43.♕b1+ ♖b3 44.♕c2+-] **34...♖xc3
35.♕e2 ♕f7 36.g5 h5** –+

[43]

▷ D. Arutinian
▶ A. Zubov
Asrian Memorial Yerevan,
24.06.2017

31...♕d7! 32.♖ad1 [32.♗c5 ♖b8
33.♕a7 (*33.♕d6 ♕b7 34.♖xf3
♕b2+-+*) 33...♖b2+ 34.♖f2 (*34.♔xf3
♕d3+ 35.♗e3 ♕e2+ 36.♔e4 ♕c2+
37.♔d5 ♖d8+ 38.♔e6 ♕c6+ 39.♔f7
♕e8#*) 34...♖xf2+ 35.♔xf2 ♕xa7
36.♗xa7 ♘xe5–+; 32.♔xf3 ♕d5+
33.♔g4 ♕g2 34.♗g1 ♖d3–+] **32...**

Nh4+ 0–1 [32...Nh4+ 33.gxh4 (33. Kg1 Qxd1 34.Rxd1 Rxd1+–+) 33... Qg4+–+]

(44)

▷ T. Burg
► B. Bok
Dutch Championship, 01.07.2017

16...Bd6! 17.dxe5 [17.Bg3 Nxd3 18.Qxd3 Rdg8–+] 17...fxe5 18.Bg5 [18.Bg3 e4 19.Kg2 Bxg3 20.hxg3 exd3 21.Qxd3 e5–+] 18...e4 19.Bxd8 Bc5+ 20.Nxc5 Qxh2# 0–1

(45)

▷ P. Ponkratov
► E. Najer
Russian Higher League, 10.07.2017

28...Nxe3! 29.Qxe3 [29.Kxe3 Bb6+ 30.Rc5 Rxc5–+] 29...Bb6 30.Rc5 Nd5! 31.Qxe4 Rfe8 32.Qd4 Nxb4 33.Nb3 Nc2 34.Qd5 Qe7 0–1

(46)

▷ R. Barski
► B. Heberla
Najdorf Memorial, 11.07.2017

28.R8d7! [28.R8d6+–] 28...Nxd7 29.Rxd7 Rd8 [29...Qxd7 30.Bxd7 Rd8 31.Ba4+–] 30.Qxg7+! 1–0 [30. Qxg7+ Qxg7 (30...Kxg7 31.Rxe7++–) 31.Rxd8+ Qg8 32.Rxg8#]

(47)

▷ Q. Ma
► Q. Liu
Chinese League, 28.07.2017

23.Re1!! Rg8 [23...g3 24.fxg3 Rg8 25.Rexe7 Rxe7 26.Bxe7+–] 24.Qxe8! gxh3+ [24...Rxe8 25.Bxe7 Qh5 (25...Kg8 26.Bxh4+–) 26.Re5+–] 25.Kh1 Rxe8 [25...Qg4 26.Qxg8+ Qxg8 27.Rg1+–] 26.Bxe7 Qh5 27.Bf6+ Kg8 28.Rg1+ Kf8 29.Bg7+ Kg8 30.Be5+ Kf8 31.Bd6+ Re7 32.Rxe7 Qf3+ 33.Kh2 1–0

(48)

▷ R. Vaganian
► Y. Hou
Biel GM, 01.08.2017

20...Bxg2! 21.Kxg2 [21.Bxg7 Rf7 22.Kxg2 Rxg7 23.Kh1 Qd5+µ] 21...Qxd4! 22.Qxg6 [22.exd4 Nf4+ 23.Kf3 Nxh5µ] 22...Qd5+ 23.e4 fxe4 24.Qxe4 [24.Bxe4 Qxd2 25.Qxh7+ Kf7 26.Qg6+ Ke7 27.Qxg7+ Rf7–+] 24...Qg5+! 25.Kh1 Qxd2 26.Qxh7+ Kf7 27.Qg6+ Ke7 28.Qxg7+ Rf7 –+

(49)

▷ Y. Zinchenko
► D. Balokas
Heraklion Gazi Open, 05.08.2017

19.f5! exf5 20.Bc4 d5 21.Re7!! Qg6 [21...Qxe7 22.Nxd5 Nxd5 23.Qxe7+–; 21...dxc4 22.Rxf7 Rxf7

23.♕xc4 ♗d7±] **22.♘xd5 ♘xd5**
23.♗xd5+ ♔h8 24.♕f4 ♕f6
25.♖fe1 +-

(50)

▷ V. Anand
► F. Caruana
Sinquefield Cup, 06.08.2017

22.exf6!! ♖xe2 [22...gxf6 23.e4+-]
23.f7+ ♔f8 24.♗xg7+! ♔xg7
25.♕c3+ ♖e5 [25...♕e5 26.♖xe2!
♕xc3 27.♖e8 ♕d4+ 28.♔f2 ♕xb4
29.f8♕++-] **26.♕d4!! ♕g5 27.♖c5**
♖xd4 28.f8♕ + ♔g6 29.♕f7+ 1–0

(51)

▷ H. Nakamura
► L. Aronian
Sinquefield Cup, 09.08.2017

33...♘xf3+!! 34.exf3 ♖a2+ 35.♗g2
♖g7 36.♖g1 ♖g3 37.♔h1 ♗h3
38.♗f1 [38.♔h2 ♖xf3–+ (38...♗xg2?
39.♘e6+ ♔f7 40.♘xf4±)] **38...**
e2 39.♗xe2 ♖xe2 40.♘d5 ♖xf3
[40...♗g2+ 41.♖xg2 ♖exg2 42.♘xf4
♖a2–+] **41.♖g6 ♖e6 –+**

(52)

▷ L. Ding
► A. Giri
Wenzhou, 09.08.2017

28...♖xg3+!! 29.♘xg3 ♘f4+
30.♔h2 [30.♔g4 ♕f6 31.h5 ♕g5#]
30...♕xh4+ 31.♔g1 ♖f6 32.♖d8+
♔h7 33.♖d2 ♖g6 34.♖g2 [34.

♖h2 ♖xg3+ 35.♔h1 ♘h3 36.♕f1
♕f4 37.♖d3 ♕g1+ 38.♕xg1 ♘xg1
39.♔xg1 ♕c1+ 40.♔f2 ♕c2+–+]
34...h5 35.♖h2 ♖xg3+ 36.♔h1
♕g5 37.♕f1 h4 38.♖e1 h3 39.♖d1
♕h5–+

(53)

▷ S. Mareco
► S. Ganguly
Spanish League, 15.08.2017

23...♖a7!! 24.♖xa7 [24.♖xc7 ♖xc7
25.♕e2 dxe4 26.dxe4 ♘h4 27.♘xh4
♕xh4 28.♕f3 ♖d3 29.♕g2 ♖xc3–+;
24.♖b1 ♘f4 25.♗xf4 exf4–+] **24...**
♗b6 25.d4 exd4 26.cxd4 ♗xa7
27.♗e3 ♗xd4!! 28.♕d3 [28.♗xd4
♘f4–+; 28.♘xd4 ♘h4 29.f3 ♕xg3+
30.♔f1 ♘xf3 31.♘xf3 ♕xf3+ 32.♗f2
dxe4–+] **28...♗xe3 29.♖xe3 ♘h4**
0–1

(54)

▷ J. Friedel
► F. Libiszewski
Washington Open, 15.08.2017

34.e5! ♖xb6 [34...♖f8 35.♗b4
♖f7 36.♖xe6 ♕xe6 37.exf6 ♖xf6
38.♕a8++-] **35.♕xa8+ ♔h7**
36.♕g2 ♖b2 37.exf6 ♗xf6 38.♖g1
♕f7 39.♕e4+ ♔h8 40.♗e3 ♖b3
41.♖f1 ♖xa3 42.♗d4 1–0

(55)

▷ Q. Le
▶ D. Navara
Saint Louis Rapid, 16.08.2017

53.f4! exf4 54.e5! ♖c3 [54...f3 55.e6 ♔f8 56.g6+-] **55.♖a8+?** [55.♖g7+! ♔h8 56.e6 ♖c8 57.♖d7 ♔g8 (57... ♖e8 58.e7 ♔g8 59.g6 hxg6 60.♖d8+-) 58.e7 ♖e8 59.g6 hxg6 60.♖d8+-] **55... ♔f7 56.♖a7+ ♔e6 –+**

(56)

▷ H. Wang
▶ X. Bu
Chinese League, 20.08.2017

32...♘xc4! 33.♗xc4 ♗a4 34.♗xe6 [34.♘xa4 ♖xc4 35.♘b2 ♖cc1 36.♘d1 ♖xd1 37.♖xd1 ♖xd1 38.♔h2 ♗e5+ 39.g3 ♖d2+ 40.♔h1 ♗xg3–+] **34... fxe6 35.♘xa4 ♖cc1 36.♖xe6 ♖xg1+ 37.♔h2 h5 38.♔g3 ♖a2 39.♘b2 ♗xb2 40.♔h2 ♖aa1 41.♔g3 ♔f7** 0–1

(57)

▷ A. Strikovic
▶ V. Sanal
Serbian League, 01.09.2017

45...♖f8!! 46.♕xf5 [46.♕e3 ♕xe3 47.♘xe3 ♗d4 48.♖e2 ♗d3 49.♖e1 ♖c8! 50.♗f1 (50.♔f2 g4–+ 51.♔g1 ♖c1–+) 50...♖c1! 51.♖xc1 ♗xe3+ 52.♔g2 ♗e4+ 53.♔h3 ♗xc1–+] **46... ♗e7!** 0–1 [46...♗e7 47.♖xc5 ♗xc5–+]

(58)

▷ B. Jobava
▶ Y. Yu
Fide World Cup Tbilisi, 08.09.2017

28.♘xf6!! ♔xf6 [28...♕xf6 29.dxe5 ♕e6 30.♘g5 ♕b3 31.e6+ ♕xb2 32.exd7 ♕d2 33.d8♕ ♕xe1 (33... ♕xd8 34.♘e6++-) 34.♕d7+ ♔h6 35.♘f7+ ♔g7 36.♘e5+ ♔h8 37.♕e8+ ♔g7 38.♕f7+ ♔h6 39.♕f8+ ♔g5 40.h4++-] **29.dxe5+ ♔f7** [29...♔e6 30.e4+-] **30.e6+! ♔xe6 31.e4** ♘g7 [31...♘d6 32.♕a2+ ♔f6 33.e5++-; 31...♘h6 32.♕e5+ ♔f7 33.♕h8 ♔e6 34.♘d4++-; 31...♘h4 32.♕a2+ ♔d6 33.e5+ ♔c7 34.♘xh4 ♕xh4 35.e6 ♖e7 36.♕c2+ ♔b8 37.♕d2+-] **32.♕a2+ ♔d6 33.♖c1!** ♗xe4 [33...♕d8 34.♕a3+ ♔e6 35.h4! h6 36.♕e3+-] **34.♕d2+ ♔e6 35.♘g5+ ♔f5 36.g4+ ♔f6 37.♘xe4+ ♕xe4 38.♕xd7 ♘e6 39.♗g2 ♕d4 40.♕xh7 ♘f4 41.♕h8+ ♔e6 42.♖e1+** 1–0

(59)

▷ M. Matlakov
▶ L. Aronian
Fide World Cup Tbilisi, 10.09.2017

20.♗xh7! ♕e5 [20...♘xh7 21.♕e6+ ♔f8 22.♗a3+ ♗e7 23.♖bc1 ♗c6 24.♘xc6 bxc6 25.♗xc6 ♕xc6 26.♗xe7+ ♔e8 27.♗d6+ ♔d8 28.♕e7#] **21.♖xb7+ ♗d7 22.♕g4!** ♕xd4 [22...♘xh7 23.♖xd7+ ♔g8 24.♘f5 ♔h8 25.♗f4+-] **23.♖xd7+ ♘xd7 24.♕xd7+ ♗e7 25.♖e1 ♕e5 26.♗d2 ♖d8 27.♕g4** 1–0

(60)

▷ J. Moussard
▶ D. Fridman

Paris Oscaro Blitz, 16.09.2017

34.♘b5! ♕c4 35.♘c7+! ♕xc7 36.♖xb7! ♘b4 37.♕b5+ ♕c6 38.♖b8+ ♔d7 39.♖d8+ ♔c7 40.♕b8# 1–0

(61)

▷ D. Naroditsky
▶ S. Shankland

Imre Konig Memorial Rapid, 17.09.2017

34.♖xa6+!! ♔xa6 [34...bxa6 35.♕xg7+ ♔b8 (35...♔a8 36.♘c7++−) 36.♕xe5++−] **35.♕a8+ ♕a7 36.♘b4+ ♔b6 37.c5+! ♔c7** [37...♘xc5 38.♕d8#] **38.♕xa7 ♖xb3 39.♕b6+ ♔c8 40.♕e6+** 1–0

(62)

▷ E. Perelshteyn
▶ D. Howell

Douglas IoM Open, 29.09.2017

47...♖gxg3+! 48.♔h4 ♔d8!! 49.f5 ♖h3+ 50.♔g4 ♖ag3+ 51.♔f4 ♖f3+ 52.♔g4 ♖fg3+ 53.♔f4 ♗e5+ 0–1

(63)

▷ V. Malakhov
▶ B. Predojevic

Croatian League, 01.10.2017

19.♖g3!! fxe5 [19...♖ae8 20.♖h3 ♕g5 21.♕c4+ ♔h8 22.♘g6++−] **20.dxe5**

♗c5 21.f6 ♗d5 [21...♖f7 22.b4 ♗f8 23.♕c4+−] **22.b4 ♗xb4 23.♖xg7+ ♔h8 24.e6 ♗d6 25.♖g3! ♖xf6 26.♕h5** 1–0

(64)

▷ B. Savchenko
▶ D. Andreikin

Russian Champ. Blitz, 02.10.2017

21.♗g6! fxg6 22.♗a3 ♔g8 23.♘xg6 [23.♗xd6!+−] **23...♗c7 24.♖xd8+ ♗xd8 25.♖d1 ♗c7 26.♘xh8 ♔xh8 27.♗d6 ♗xd6 28.♖xd6±**

(65)

▷ G. Sargissian
▶ S. Bogner

European Team Champ., 28.10.2017

23.♕g4!! [23.♕c4 ♗b4 24.♕c6 ♕e8³] **23...f5 24.♕e2! ♖h8 25.♕c4 ♗b4** [25...♗a3 26.♕xa4 ♗xc1 27.♘xc1±] **26.♕c6 ♘c5** [26...♕e8 27.♖d7+−] **27.♘xc5 ♖ac8** [27...♖fc8 28.♕b7+−] **28.♖d7 ♖xc6 29.♖xe7 ♖g8 30.♗d4** 1–0

(66)

▷ M. Tabatabaei
▶ G. Sibashvili

Teheran Paytakht Cup, 30.10.2017

19.♖h4! [19.♘xd6 ♕xd6 20.♖h4 ♔g8 21.♖xd4 ♕h2 22.♕xg6+−] **19...♔h8** [19...♔g8 20.♖xh5 gxh5 21.♘f6+ gxf6 22.♕g6+ ♔h8 23.♕h6+ ♔g8 24.g6+−] **20.♘xd6 ♕xd6 21.♗c2**

♔g8 22.♖xh5 ♕h2 23.0-0-0
♕xf2 24.exd4 ♖fe8 25.♖f1 1–0

(67)

▷ J. Bai
► L. Ding
Chinese League, 04.11.2017

23...♖d2! 24.♕b3 [24.♕xd2
♘e4+ 25.♔h4 ♗xd2–+] 24...♘e4+
25.♔h4 [25.♔f4 ♖xf2+ 26.♔xe4
♗f5+ 27.♔d5 ♗e6+ 28.♔e4 f5+
29.♔d3 ♖d2#] 25...♗e7+ 26.♔xh5
♔g7 27.♗f4 ♗f5 28.♗h6+ ♔h7
29.♕xb7 ♖xf2 30.♗g5 ♖h8
31.♘xf7 ♗g6+ 32.♔xg4 ♘e5+
0–1[32...♘e5+ 33.♘xe5 ♗f5+ 34.♔h5
♔g7+ 35.♗h6+ ♖xh6#]

(68)

▷ R. Rapport
► D. Howell
European Team Champ., 06.11.2017

34.♘f6+!! gxf6 35.♕g3+ ♔f8
36.exf6 ♕b4 37.♕xc7 ♕xh4+
[37...♔g8 38.♕g3++–] 38.♔g1 ♕xf6
39.♕c8+ ♔g7 40.♕g4+ +–

(69)

▷ H. Asis Gargatagli
► A. Alonso Rosell
Barcelona GM, 09.11.2017

14.♘xh7! ♔xh7 15.h5 ♔g7
16.hxg6 fxg6 17.♘e5 ♖f5 18.♘xg6
♗g5+ 19.f4 ♘xc4 [19...♔xg6 20.g4
♗xf4+ 21.♔b1 ♘xc4 22.gxf5+ exf5

23.♕xc4+–] 20.♕h3! ♕g8 [20...
♔xg6 21.♕h7+ ♔f6 22.fxg5++–]
21.fxg5 ♔f7 [21...♔xg6 22.g4+–
] 22.g4 ♕xg6 23.gxf5 ♕xg5+
24.♔b1 ♔e7 25.♕h8 +–

(70)

▷ P. Ponkratov
► A. Goganov
Ugra Governor's Cup Blitz, 23.11.2017

34.♗b4! ♖xd1 35.♖xd1 1–0[35.
♖xd1 ♗xb4 36.♖d8+ ♖e8 37.♖xe8+
♗f8 38.e7+–]

(71)

▷ D. Howell
► L. McShane
British ко Championship, 09.12.2017

25...♘g4! 26.♘e4 [26.♖xe7 ♖xe7
27.♘e4 ♗d4–+; 26.hxg4 ♕xg4+
27.♔h2 ♕xh4+ 28.♔g2 ♗d4–+]
26...♗xh4 27.♘xd6 ♕d7 28.♖xe7
♖xe7 29.♘e4 ♕f5 30.♗d3 ♘xf4+
31.♗xf4 ♕xf4 32.hxg4 ♕xg4+
[32...f5 33.♘f2 ♖e3–+] 33.♔f1 ♕f3+
34.♔g1 f5 35.♕h2 ♕xd3 36.♘c5
♕d4+ 37.♔h1 ♕xc5 38.♖g1
♕xg1+ 0–1

(72)

▷ V. Plat
► K. Szadkowski
European Champ. Rapid, 16.12.2017

25.g4! ♕xf4 26.♘f6+ 1–0[26.♘f6+
♕xf6 27.♕e8+ ♖xe8 28.♖xe8#]